CW00802485

8

THEME AND VARIATIONS
MUSICAL NOTES BY A NEUROLOGIST

THEME AND VARIATIONS

MUSICAL NOTES BY A NEUROLOGIST

CARL ELLENBERGER, M.D.

SUNACUMEN
PRESS
PALM SPRINGS, CA

Copyright 2018 © Carl Ellenberger
All rights reserved.
Second Edition.

No part of this publication may be reproduced, stored in a retrieval system,
or transmitted, in any form or by any means, without the prior permission in
writing of Carl Ellenberger, or as expressly permitted by law.

The author and publisher of this book do not, through its publication, dispense
medical advice or prescribe the use of any technique as a form of treatment
for physical or medical issues. The intent of the author and publisher is to offer
information of a general nature to help readers in their quest for emotional and
spiritual well-being.

Cover design and formatting: Sunacumen Press

Hardcover edition 2019
Published by Sunacumen Press
Palm Springs, CA

LCCN: 2018958705

Publisher's Cataloging-In-Publication Data
(Prepared by The Donohue Group, Inc.)
Names: Ellenberger, Carl, author.
Title: Theme and variations : musical notes by a neurologist / Carl Ellenberger, M.D.
Description: Palm Springs, CA : Sunacumen Press, [2018] | Includes bibliographical
references.
Identifiers: Harcover ISBN: 978-0-9995612-4-9
Paperback ISBN: 978-0-9995612-3-2
Subjects: LCSH: Music--Psychological aspects. | Music--Physiological aspects. | Music
therapy. | Cognitive neuroscience. | Ellenberger, Carl--Knowledge--Music.
Classification: LCC ML3830 .E45 2018 | DDC 781.11--dc23
Printed in U.S.A.

To Emi

TABLE OF CONTENTS

Don Pedro:

> Now, pray thee, come;
> Or, if thou wilt hold longer argument,
> Do it in notes.

Balthasar:

> Note this before my notes;
> There's not a note of mine that's worth the noting.

Don Pedro:

> Why, these are very crotchets that he speaks;
> Note, notes, forsooth, and nothing.

— Shakespeare, *Much Ado About Nothing*, Act II, Scene 3

INTRODUCTION

If you are looking about for really profound mysteries, essential aspects of our existence for which neither the sciences nor the humanities can provide any sort of explanation, I suggest you start with music. The professional musicologists, tremendous scholars all, for whom I have the greatest respect, haven't a ghost of an idea about what music is, or how the human mind makes music on its own, before it is written down and played. The biologists are no help here, nor the psychologists, nor the physicists, nor the philosophers, wherever they are these days. Nobody can explain it. It is a mystery, and thank goodness for that.

Since a late medical colleague of mine, Dr. Lewis Thomas, wrote those words in 1980,[1] scientists have stepped up efforts to understand his mystery. What, and *why*, is music?

Such scientists—biologists, psychologists, and physicists as well as philosophers—answer now to the new appellation "neuroscientist." They have applied new methods made possible by a growing critical mass of interest and data—the latter a product of the digital revolution, including the ability to see the living brain at work using functional magnetic resonance imaging (fMRI) in real time.

Still hindered by a lack of definitions, standards, curricula, or even common language, and representing almost a dozen biological disciplines and medical specialties conjoined under a huge umbrella, these diverse investigators are pioneers in a burgeoning new field that some call *neuromusic*. If as eminent a biologist as E. O. Wilson can speak of the neuroscience of religion,[2] then we can also speak of the neuroscience of music. And we can agree with another notable neuroscientist, who said:

> [G]rowing evidence from neuroscience . . . suggests that music
> is biologically powerful, meaning that it can have lasting effects
> on nonmusical abilities (such as language or attention) during
> the lifetime of individual humans. Importantly, these effects can
> be observed not only in trained musicians but also in ordinary
> individuals who engage regularly with music. Thus I believe
> that music should be regarded as a biologically powerful human
> invention or "transformative technology of the mind."[3]

As a student unable to choose which career to enter, I chose two: medicine and music. It's no surprise that I never became a superstar in either field, but I did receive an ample share of fulfillment—especially welcome in a medical specialty, neurology, that is one of several reporting high rates of burnout since I finished my education.[4] As a neurologist and musician (like Oliver Sacks, my model of a good neurologist), I have only late in my career stepped into the realm of the neuroscience of music—a field perhaps inhabited even more by psychologists than by neurologists—and become interested in the effect of music on human development, health, and well-being at all ages. In this book, I examine the interfaces between music, brain science, and clinical medicine to find synergy among those fields and try to apply what I have learned.

Part One, *Exploring Music in the Brain*, discusses what I have learned by bringing my experience in clinical neurology and neuroscience to my new interest in how and why the brain processes music and what the proper place for music is in our lives—extending to education, to therapy for certain conditions, and to our overall fulfillment. Part Two, *Reflections on a Musical Life,* explores some of the life experiences that inspired my interest in neuromusic.

In our world of rapid and accelerating technological change, what is the proper place for music? Is it just for occasional entertainment, or as background to our daily lives? In defiance of either fate, I try both to demonstrate the power of music to enable us to better study the brain, and to show how learning how the brain perceives music can help us better understand the brain, music, and ourselves. New thinking and experiments in the field of gene-cultural co-evolution have contributed an exciting new perspective regarding these questions. Not only do our genes determine the structure of our bodies and much of our behavior, but our culture has done so, too: Culture and external factors can shape our genes as well as our lives. "Human minds are not just built for culture; they are built by culture."[5]

Human culture, in which music has played a major part, has actually influenced our biological evolution. The part of the brain called the neocortex has not only expanded during human evolution (quadrupling in size in the last three million years) but become infinitely more complex under the influence of our culture, especially in the regions linked to innovation, imitation, tool use, and language. And what is music but an example of innovation, imitation, tool use, and language? It is no surprise, then, that we are beginning to learn that music practice promotes increased brain volume, and that music can impel a structural reorganization of the brain that can lead to increased complexity—not only in the course of evolution, but also during our individual lives [chapters 1–3].

Music as therapy for a range of conditions was pioneered by the great Oliver Sacks.[6] I explore recent developments in this field in Alzheimer's, Parkinson's, and stroke patients and also among musicians who contract the condition of dystonia, which can end their careers [chapters 4–11]. In all of the chapters in Part One, references guide readers deeper into more developments in each field of inquiry.

In chapters 12–16, I try to understand the enormous changes in music performance and listening that have taken place during my life-time. As an adolescent, I aspired to sit in an orchestra, like the Cleveland Orchestra in my hometown, in the same seat one of my teachers held for fifty years. But the music that orchestra makes today, though to some sophisticated ears played at an even higher level, is no longer what most people mean when they play, or speak of, music. That's because of a huge change in the demographics of the people they play *for*. Performing arts organizations of all sizes, from the small Music at Gretna—the musical organization I began decades ago in Mount Gretna, Pennsylvania* (also called by its trade name, Gretna Music)—to the massive Metropolitan Opera in New York City, scramble to retain audiences to support their missions without having to drain dry the wells of patronage or tap endowments. At the same time, a few celebrity soloists and more than a few rock and pop-star entertainers receive millions of dollars to play at big events like the Coachella Festival and the Super Bowl. For too many people, our music tends to be classical in the worst sense of that term: old music, outmoded and forgotten. I find myself a little sheepish when I respond to the question: "What kind of music do you play?" The response to my answer, "classical and jazz," is usually a conversation-stopping "Oh."

I hope to convince readers that there are valid reasons to study music—to read it, play it, sing it, and learn about all of its power—at a young age. Music is not just entertainment for later years, like watching sitcoms and sports on TV. I wish I could have written what Adam Gopnik wrote in *The New Yorker* about an earlier time in *his* life:

> *Music represented for me not the endless, shifting weather-cover of sound that it does for my kids, a cloud in every sense, a perpetual availability of emotion to suit a mood and moment. Music meant difficulty—and, when the difficulty was overcome, the possibilities of life, too. It was something to master.*[7]

As it turned out, much of my music playing and listening happened

---

* www.gretnamusic.org

in forests around lakes, experiences that I recount in chapters 17 and 18 to begin Part Two. A forest, we are beginning to learn, is a special place.[8] Perhaps that weird aspect of my life informs my views in this volume, as does the fact that I also spent so much time in forests thinking about the brain.

In my view, the style, genre, and age of whatever music is performed means less than the actual performance of it. Written notes are simply lifeless symbols, though elements of an important language according to Leonard Bernstein,[9] Deryck Cooke,[10] and Ani Patel[11]—or "creative play when sound meets human imagination."[12] The art of music requires a performer's effective communication through that language with other human beings, in real time or in recordings, including the ability to "penetrate the heart" rather than "only reach the ear," in the words of the eighteenth-century music chronicler Charles Burney.[13] With classical music we will always have the additional challenge of making music written sometime in the past four centuries speak to contemporary listeners—much as T. S. Eliot wrote about the need, in poetry, to give a sense "not only of the pastness of the past, but of its presence," its timelessness.[14] And that was before the digital, wireless, mp3 generation presented an entirely new and hostile environment for the works of Bach, Beethoven, and even Gershwin.

Classical music is one wherein the notes are written by a composer who may not be the performer, with the expectation that they will be followed more or less exactly. Toscanini espoused that rule, and the longevity (or continued success of cultural transmission) of many of the particular classical works in what is called the canon probably relates directly to some degree of fidelity of the performance to the composer's intent, as expressed in the original written score. But at the same time, the effectiveness of a performance cannot be judged only on the basis of how close to literalness the performer came. There is also this:

[W]hat really moves us in music is the vital sign of a human hand, in all its unsteady and broken grace. (Too much imperfection and it sounds like a madman playing; too little, and

it sounds like a robot.) Ella singing Gershwin matters because
Ella knows when to make the words warble. . . . The art is the
perfected imperfection.
   — *Adam Gopnik*[15]

This may have been suggested more succinctly in a lyric by Irving Mills (music by Duke Ellington) sung by Ella herself, along with many others:

It don't mean a thing if it ain't got that swing.

Or as an eminent musicologist has it:

Being the true voice of one's time is . . . roughly forty thousand
times as vital and important as being the assumed voice of
history. To be the expressive medium of one's own age is . . . a
far worthier aim than historical verisimilitude. What is verisi-
militude, after all, but perceived correctness? And correctness
is the paltriest of virtues. It is something to demand of students,
not artists.[16]

So another consideration with respect to eliciting an engaged response to classical music is that the quality of the performance of any work of music is critical to its success. A listener at an amateur or student concert may say, "I don't like classical music," when she or he could more accurately say, "I wasn't moved by that particular performance." In truth, it wasn't the music; it was the performance that fell short. And playing classical music well takes not just talent and awareness of tradition, but more than ten thousand hours of hard practice to learn.[17] (No music illustrates that principle better than some of the compositions of Franz Liszt, say the Hungarian Rhapsodies, that can fall flat under the fingers of an amateur.)

Music at Gretna has always identified excellent performance as our most important mission as we explore an ever-expanding range of music, from the medieval era to our time and whether composed in the United States or anywhere else in the world. My assumption when I began this small organization forty-three years ago was that if *any* music is played well, an audience will come.

In some of the essays in chapters 17–28 I explore the power of music in my life and in the lives of others whom I have known, and provide the broad context for my interest in "neuromusic." In these chapters and throughout the book, with general readers in mind who are neither musicians nor scientists, I have tried to follow the advice of Albert Einstein: "Things should be made as simple as possible, but not any simpler."

Do I think that my interest and involvement in music has made me a better doctor? I am always asked that question. I like to think, with no evidence at all, that it has at least made me a better person. I believe music had such an effect on the great Oliver Sacks:

> *Both his science and his life were undergirded by a profound reverence for music—music seemed to be this intellectual giant's greatest form of spirituality. He knew that the life of the mind and the life of the body were one, and understood that music married the two—an understanding he carried in his synapses and his sinews.*[18]

Despite all the efforts discussed in this book and far more that are not, we have made only small progress toward explaining Lewis Thomas's mystery of music. But during what seem to some the declining years of the American experiment and when the future of the planet has been called into question, music and the arts can, I hope, do much to sustain us, and thereby become more important than ever. And I also hope that the reader does not conclude that I have committed the error in which "Truth is replaced by Useful Knowledge."* Instead I have attempted to explore and convey the part of the Truth that has enriched my life.

---

* W.H. Auden, *Under Which Lyre: A Reactionary Tract for the Times.*

Music, uniquely among the arts, is both completely abstract and profoundly emotional. It has no power to represent anything particular or external, but it has a unique power to express inner states or feelings. Music can pierce the heart directly; it needs no mediation. One does not have to know anything about Dido and Aeneas to be moved by her lament for him; anyone who has ever lost someone knows what Dido is expressing. And there is, finally, a deep and mysterious paradox here, for while such music makes one experience pain and grief more intensely, it brings solace and consolation at the same time.

—Oliver Sacks,
Musicophilia: Tales of Music and the Brain

Part One

Of all the amazing things the mind does, the most amazing may be that it can take sound and turn it into music, and then take music and turn it into meaning. The rest of the double leaps the mind makes look almost easy by comparison: we like pictures of babies at picnics in sunlight because, after all, in the world we like sunny days and chubby babies. The stories we tell in literature are like the lies we tell in life. But music is simply a set of physical vibrations that reach our eardrums; from those vibrations we make the emotional map of our lives.

— Adam Gopnik, in *The New Yorker*

1

Why There is Music

I t *is* all in your head.

Because music began in Paleolithic times. . . and because it re-
mains universal in hunter-gatherer societies around the world,
it is reasonable to conclude that our loving devotion to it has
been hardwired by evolution in the human brain.[19]

When given a choice between listening to music versus silence, our
close evolutionary relatives (tamarins and marmosets) generally prefer
silence.[20]

What theory explains why *Homo sapiens*, almost alone among species, have made music since the origin of their species? A quick, simple
answer, explored later, is that few if any species other than *Homo sa-*
piens have evolved the brain capacity necessary to experience pleasure
from music. Monkeys, for example, lack our working auditory memory
needed to remember sounds.[21] They couldn't whistle a tune (even if they
could whistle), or remember music again after they have heard it. But
let's start from the beginning.

The earliest known musical instrument is a bird-bone flute dating
back approximately forty-five thousand years, found in the German site

of Geißenklösterle,[22] but the breathing apparatus required to play it—and to sing—had evolved far earlier.[23] So we can safely assume that singing preceded that time and began closer to—or even before—the start of the "*Homo sapiens* advantage" around seventy thousand years ago, "when our ancestors dispersed from Africa, to ultimately replace all other humans and reach the farthest corners and most extreme environments of the earth." Archeologist Steven Mithen further theorizes that the reason for that advantage wasn't brain size, because the size of Neanderthals' brains matched that of *Homo sapiens*'.[24] Instead, he continues, "My guess is that it may have been another invention: perhaps symbolic art that could extend the power of those eight-six billion neurons or maybe new forms of connectivity that provided the capacity for language." One might further speculate, music being both an art and a language[25] and both faculties being unique to humans, that language too played a critical part in bringing about the advantage that led, eventually, to seven billion *Homo sapiens* taking over our planet. And results from rapidly progressing genetic studies may eventually replace speculation.[26]

This question about why, among billions of species, *Homo sapiens* virtually appropriated the entire planet for themselves is a common and current question and a frequent subject of books, increasingly pondered and researched with modern methods since Lewis Thomas's ambivalent ruminations regarding why we "haven't a ghost of an idea of what music is" in *On Matters of Doubt* in 1980. We still have few definitive answers but are perhaps inching closer to them. But, again in Thomas's wise words in the same book, "conclusions reached in science are always, when looked at closely, far more provisional and tentative than are most of the assumptions arrived at by our colleagues in the humanities."[27]

Moving from questions about why *Homo sapiens* is the only species (with a few arguable exceptions) that plays and listens to music to questions about why individual humans do so seems to be the next logical step. Both questions seem interrelated, at least to this non-anthropologist. Unless you are content with Johann Sebastian Bach's view that music was "especially ordered by God's spirit through David,"[28] one category of answers to the question of why music exists, maybe the most intuitive, holds that music (and dance, which was inseparable from music until recent centuries) confers an evolutionary selective advantage on those humans who make it or listen to it.[29] Proving selective advantage is a very difficult proposition, but it is always fun, and useful, to speculate about it. What might such an advantage consist in, and how strong might it be? Some, not mutually exclusive possibilities, include:

1. A simple one: Music is sexy and promotes procreation. That was Darwin's view, though he paid little attention to music. Humans who can sing and dance are perhaps more attractive mates and hence potentially may produce more offspring. (Think "rock star" Beyoncé—or "old" Bach and his twenty children.) But most scientific studies attempting to find a connection between musicality and "sexual success" have failed to find one.

2. Music, like all languages, can be learned most easily by the young developing brain, before the brain can handle more complex disciplines, like string theory or quantum mechanics. It exercises the brain early (even in preschool) to develop certain abilities and skills when the brain is most receptive or plastic, and the brain then gains capacities that peers, coming a year or two later to kindergarten, may never acquire. Perfect (or absolute) pitch, a capacity that must be acquired early during the first decade, is an example that, as we will see, can later be a useful quality.

3. Another theory holds that musical sounds were *Homo sapiens'* first language, possibly primarily to communicate emotions rather than information and carried over from pre-human ancestors, like those who play in Bernie Krause's *The Great Animal Orchestra*.[30] Eventually, spoken language, providing more precise communication of data and information, prevailed for those purposes, while music continued as: a) an alternative method of communication (that doesn't lie [Jimi Hendrix*]; speaks when words fail [Hans Christian Anderson**]; or expresses

* Hendrix: "Music doesn't lie. If there is something to be changed in this world, then it can only happen through music."
** Anderson: "Where words fail, music speaks."

thoughts too definite or precise for words [Felix Mendelssohn*]; b) an enhancement to emotions, especially when combined with speech; or c) just an unnecessary vestigial skill or evolutionary by-product, the "auditory cheesecake" of psychologist Steven Pinker (who may have intended to challenge someone to prove that he was wrong).[31]

Noting that music and dance coexist in every culture on earth, and in light of embodied cognition studies,[32] noted jazz pianist Vijay Iyer reminds us that "music is first and foremost the sounds of us doing stuff with our bodies; and so when you hear music, you're hearing other bodies moving . . . somebody is doing something. Music is somehow an auditory trace of human activity."[33] A recent book by Mark Changizi (*Harnessed: How Language and Music Mimicked Nature and Transformed Ape to Man* [BenBella Books, 2011]) makes the case, according to Iyer, that we are evolutionarily attuned to hear each other in our midst, and that music is made up of the rhythms of bodies in motion.

4. Music is an inborn human need, like religion—which is also a strictly human characteristic that partakes of mystery and relates to the search for meaning and understanding, and which also dates to our beginnings. "In almost all living societies, from hunter-gatherer to civilized-urban, there exists an intimate relation between music and religion. Are there genes for religiosity that prescribe a neural and biochemical mediation like that of music? Yes, says evidence from the relatively young discipline of the neuroscience of religion."[34] Indeed, we have this recent discovery: "We demonstrate using functional magnetic resonance imaging scans in nineteen devout Mormons that a recognizable feeling central to their devotional practice was repeatedly associated with activation in nucleus accumbens, ventromedial prefrontal cortex, and frontal attentional regions"[35]—which happen to be regions that music also activates.

Now let's get further from speculation and closer to some developments in modern science. It seems reasonable to assume that music enhances social cohesion and thus increases survival of individual humans.[36] A part of that advantage lies in the nurturing of infants and

* Mendelssohn: "It's not that music is too imprecise for words, but too precise."

children. Lullabies and nursery rhymes express motherly love and help infants survive and thrive; these songs can be found in almost any culture.[37] Older humans sing together to strengthen social bonds: That's why we have singing Rotary clubs and choirs in schools and churches, as recounted in Stacy Horn's heartwarming memoir, which recounts how singing in a good church choir changed her life, her social life, her mood, and her health.[38] We train our military with extensive synchronous marching, often with music, because the synchronous activity entrains individuals' neural circuitry, enabling them to connect their perception of others' performing an action to their own performance, thereby promoting intra-group bonding. Scientists speak of the "social facilitation effect"—a kind of teamwork, perhaps. Groups of soldiers who sing or chant when running can run farther, faster, and with less pain, and bond with each other in the process.[39] And beyond music, in the words of Jamshed Bharucha, *all* creative domains "enable human beings to connect; to form groups that synchronize each other emotionally; to synchronize their brains and create a sense of group identity . . . "[40]

This avenue of inquiry has become even more interesting in the past decade. Shortly after Darwin's monumental discoveries recorded in *The Origin of the Species*, Alfred Russel Wallace, writing in 1870, put his finger on an important question: What is the "power, distinct from that which has guided the development of the lower animals, that allowed humans to far outpace on the development scale all of their closest ancestral relatives?"[41] (Wallace actually invoked Bach's divine creator to answer his question.) Or, in modern terms, "[H]ow did our ancestors make the journey from apes scavenging a living on ants, tubers, and nuts, to modern humans able to compose symphonies, perform ballet, and design particle accelerators?"[42] In other words, how did *Homo sapiens* bridge the great gap between the highest primates living now, most still in the forest cracking nuts and fishing for ants and honey, to become humans who dominate the world through our technological, artistic, architectural, linguistic, and other achievements, which together enable an extraordinarily potent capacity to modify the circumstances of our lives? (See these books.[43]) "Rachmaninoff's piano concertos," notes Kevin Laland, "did not evolve by the laws of natural selection. . . . ”[44]

A better answer than Wallace's had to await the understanding of gene behavior that we have achieved in the past decades. It includes, in particular, the revelation that genes (or our *genome*, the entire collection of such) are not a permanent, inherited, inflexible recipe directing the development of each individual human but rather are *modifiable*, at all ages, in response to human behavior as well as external factors. Laland likens genes to children's building blocks: "broadly similar blocks that are assembled in different species in dissimilar ways. Human and chimpanzee genes could be exactly identical and still work differently because they can be turned on and off to different degrees, in different places, or at different times."[45] Over the past decade, scientists have become aware of the central role in evolution played by culture, the "extensive accumulation of shared, learned knowledge, and iterative improvements in technology over time."[46] They have coined the term "gene-culture co-evolution" to indicate that genes and culture can shape each other's characteristics. Humans are "eusocial" animals: This means that our division of labor as well as group loyalty reach a point where the group essentially operates as a unit of evolutionary selection—as an orchestra, as opposed to a ragtag band of undisciplined self-servers. And we can literally build "the landscape for our further evolution" as our extraordinary capacity for culture continues to expand. Social learning, especially by means of imitating and copying others, is critical to that process—as is, of course, language, one of our unique human abilities.[47]

For a simple example of gene-culture co-evolutionary interaction, consider lactose tolerance, one of the strongest, and best studied examples of the response of human genes exposed to culturally modified conditions. It is the story of the coevolution of dairy farming, and associated consumption of dairy products, the cultural part, with gene alleles that allow humans to digest lactose, the sugar in milk.[48] In most humans (and other animals), the ability to metabolize lactose disappears in childhood, but in at least six separate cultural groups, the activity of lactase (the metabolizing enzyme) persists into adulthood. This lactose tolerance results from a mutation at a single genetic focus. Lactose-tolerance alleles (gene variations) have spread from low to high frequencies in less than nine thousand years since the inception of dairy farming and milk consumption, an extraordinarily short time on the evolutionary calendar. One of the strongest responses to natural selection ever detected, the mutation allows humans to survive on calories from a new source, the animals they herd.

A more complex example of gene-cultural coevolution is the story of how and why left-handedness persists in human culture. Along with lactose tolerance that story is part of the "compelling case that culture is not just a product, but also a codirector of human evolution.[49] Efforts of this kind may, in the not too distant future, provide examples of how music in a particular culture can influence genes. That effort will be far more difficult because no one has any clue to what music sounded like nine thousand years ago!

In prehistoric times, evolution was almost exclusively biological: Nature selected from a random diversity of characteristics those most suited to increase the potential for survival of each species. But as humans began to develop more and more complex societies and cultures, those societies and cultures themselves played an increasing role in the evolution of our species. Concurrent with this evolution of the evolutionary process, so to speak, has been the extraordinary growth of the part of the human brain called the neocortex. That part of the brain has not only expanded over millions of years but become infinitely more complex, especially, as I noted, in the regions linked to innovation, imitation, tool use, and language. By studying the response of the brain to making music over relatively short periods (like years) via modern imaging techniques, we can almost convert evolution into real time: We can see the great white matter tract between hemispheres, the *corpus callosum*, enlarging in pianists, and the area of the cerebral cortex representing the fingers of a violinist expanding with practice, along with many other examples (more of which are in chapter 2).

Rather than ask the question "Why is music?" or "Does music serve a purpose?" maybe we should say that music is one of many characteristics, language being another, that has made humans human—as in, distinct from other species—and that will continue to do so.

In recent decades, neuroscience has begun to offer other answers to the questions above. A key reward for humans who seek out music—whether to listen to or to play—is the pleasure derived from those activities. It has long been accepted that musical pleasure involves the "whole person . . . cognitive, emotional, sensational, and behavioral at once."[50] You might even call that "rapture . . . a joy excessive and sweet"— as Spain's great mystic, Saint Teresa of Avila, described it in her 1563–65 diary—achieved variously by music, religion, and hallucinogenic drugs, such as the Amazonian religion enhancer ayahuasca, all associated with the release of the neurotransmitter, dopamine, and perhaps others.[51]

The brain links "pleasure" to "reward." Music, we have learned, can activate a reward system deep in the brain. Called "phylogenetically old" because it exists in our very distant ancestors and forms early in human ontogeny (the development of the embryo), this mesolimbic-striatal system* also promotes other adaptive survival behaviors, like eating pleasure for sustenance, sexual pleasure for procreation, and the like. The system includes interconnecting circuits and centers, like the nucleus accumbens, that *anticipate* or *predict* rewards, and to the degree that the predictions are met, produces the transmitter dopamine in the corpus striatum. Fulfillment of prediction leads to dopamine release in amounts proportional to the degree of fulfillment.[52]

"Frisson"—also sometimes called "thrills" or "chills"—may be the best word for an extreme moment of such rapture, of the sort I experience in a range of degrees during an Abbado Lucerne Festival performance of a Mahler symphony. Such sensations "integrate emotional intensity with verifiable tactile sensations not localized to any one region of the body."[53] I haven't inquired, but I suspect that most frissons may last about as long as an orgasm.

Studies have shown functional and anatomical interconnections be-

---

* The mesolimbic pathway is a collection of dopaminergic (i.e., dopamine-releasing) neurons that project from the ventral tegmental area (VTA) to the ventral striatum, which includes the nucleus accumbens (NAcc) and olfactory tubercle.

tween the auditory cortex in the lateral surface of both temporal lobes—the brain's receiving and initial processing area for sound, including music—and the reward circuitry deep in the brain. Such studies have also shown increased connectivity between the reward system and emotional and social processing areas in the insula and medial prefrontal cortex.[54] Because these interconnections providing access to the reward system vary in strength, the variability may underlie individual differences in the response to music: stronger in people who say they love music—at least the kind of music they have learned to love; weaker in those who derive less pleasure from music, and especially weak or perhaps absent in those with "musical anhedonia" (the inability to experience music as pleasurable).[55] (More about connections, connectivity, and anhedonia in chapter 2.) One group of investigators views this as "the first evidence for a neural basis of individual differences in sensory access to the reward system," which suggests, they argue, "that social-emotional communication through the auditory channel may offer an evolutionary basis for music making as an aesthetically rewarding function in humans."[56]

The results of a clever study provided intriguing validation of these hypotheses. Investigators administered the drug Naltrexone, used increasingly by emergency rooms and first responders to counteract the life-threatening effects of excess opioids. They found that the drug can also create a temporary anhedonia for music, presumably by blocking the effects of naturally occurring opioids in the brain.[57] After administration of Naltrexone, but not of an inactive control substance, subjects in the experiment lost the pleasure that usually accompanied listening to their favorite music. (Like most experiments, these need repetition for confirmation of results.)

Many pleasures—great sex, seeing cute babies, eating sweet peaches, enjoying fragrant flowers, back-scratching—come naturally with minimal or no effort needed to prepare for their enjoyment, at least when they are available. Presumably, most humans are born with strong enough connections to activate their pleasure circuits in the context of these common experiences. But deriving pleasure from the organized sound called music appears to require at least a little learning or experience, most effectively during the first two decades of life (as discussed in chapter 3). Such learning is required to prepare another system in the brain, namely the auditory and valuation-related parts of the neocortex, a part of the brain most recently and highly evolved in humans (specifically in the auditory region in the superior temporal cortex and prefrontal cortex), so as to effectively interact with the older reward system.

An extreme example of this learning process *not* working with respect to music would be a person, unusual in our time when we live in a cloud of music, but maybe exemplified in the nineteenth century by someone who heard little music when growing up, like perhaps Charles Darwin (see epigraph chapter 5). In the absence of early musical experience, such an individual's prefrontal cortex would not have developed any machinery to evaluate and understand music and poor, if any, connections to carry the resulting little bits of information to the reward system. Darwin, of course, programmed his prefrontal cortex with other information and abilities.

Other arts that give pleasure—fine art, for example, which exists in space—remain in existence indefinitely, so memory, though still necessary to our response to it, plays a less critical role: A Georgia O'Keefe flower is there to see anytime one enters a museum or looks at a print. But each note or chord of music, existing in *time*, happens (or "happened," before recordings) once and then is gone. For the brain to make anything of that note or chord, it must relate it to other notes or chords that came before and after—that is, to its context in melodies, harmony, and rhythm. Thus, the brain must have a system to *store* the sounds in short- and long-term memory for further evaluation, a system called "auditory memory." Musical memory is one kind of auditory memory. Recordings, of course, now often and plentifully feed our musical memory banks.

Musical memory is essential to listening to music, enjoying it, or composing or playing music. Bach traveled many hours to hear Buxtehude play the organ and had to carry home in his brain most of what he heard, except perhaps for a few notes jotted down on paper (also written from short-term memory immediately after he heard them). Without musical memory, you might hear a concert but, lacking any memory of the music you heard, you have little incentive to hear another, other than the (non-musical) memory of enjoying it, as you would, at a more primitive level from deeper in the brain, remember a delicious chocolate cake. A child couldn't ever learn to sing "Mary Had a Little Lamb." You couldn't remember any difference between an Adele song and a Schubert *Lied*, or what a guitar sounds like.

When finishing reading a novel or watching a movie, if you can't remember its beginning, then the ending has far less meaning. Likewise with respect to hearing the last movement of a sonata or symphony. Like an Alzheimer's patient, you would encounter new and strange sounds every day! So another reason that animals do not make or listen to music is that they don't have this kind of memory. They do not communicate about phenomena that are not immediately present. I believe it's fair to state—wearing my musician hat and without consulting any double-blind, controlled, scientific studies—a general rule: "The better the musical memory, the better the musician." (Note that I didn't say "entertainer.") On only slightly less solid ground, a corollary might be, "and the more sophisticated or fulfilled the listener." Almost needless to say, by supplementing natural musical memory, the advent of artificial musical memory in the form of *recordings*—a revolutionary change—has become a great boon to the learning, playing, composing, and enjoying of music. And recordings have also disseminated all forms of music far beyond their original evanescent, one-time existence. Books like *Reinventing Bach* by Paul Elie have explored the revolutionary effects of recordings.[58]

Musical memory alone, however, is not sufficient for getting the maximum reward from music. More complex programming of the neocortex, by means of broad and diverse experience and systematic study of music (ideally early in life), is necessary—and the more, the better. Musical memory alone does deliver a low level of reward, which is apparent when an audience breaks into applause and cheers in response to the opening notes of a familiar encore, or when a stadium packed with teenagers goes crazy as a rock band breaks into their most popular hit.

Composers in previous centuries played to musical memory with frequent repeat signs and *da capo* (meaning "back to the beginning") notation. Repetition to immediately increase familiarity was especially favored by Baroque and Classical-era composers and listeners. With all forms of memory, the storage banks of memory must be fed. And those banks are more receptive and (like your IRA) more effective, the earlier in life they are stocked. (More about critical and sensitive periods in chapter 3.) It may be useful to think of a "musical lexicon" (a term coined by Isabelle Peretz[59]) which represents a storage system for musical information that an individual has been exposed to throughout life. The lexicon includes information about relationships between sounds and the syntactic rules of musical structure specific to prior experiences. This storage system may contain "templates" that can be applied to incoming sound information to help the individual better categorize and understand what he or she is hearing. Each time a sequence of sounds is heard, several templates may be activated to fit the incoming auditory information. This process may be confirmed or violated, and will ultimately determine its reward value to the individual.[60]

So, to deliver rewards, the reward system must interact with a highly evolved, complex cognitive system that has been deliberately and effectively (even systematically, in ear-training classes) programmed not only to remember but also to analyze, evaluate, and otherwise comprehend music, and to formulate expectations with regard to it. This cognitive system, acquired over a long process of evolution, separates *Homo sapiens* from all other species and accounts for our fascination with music. The more intensely and longer these interactions take place in any individual, the stronger the reward.

But now that you may be convinced that music is a result of an evolutionary selective advantage, it turns out that not all scientists support that theory. Aniruddh Patel argues instead that "music is an invention that builds on diverse, pre-existing brain functions, rather than a trait that originated via processes of natural selection."[61]

His alternative "transformative technology of the mind" (TTM) theory holds that music is a technology that is learned anew by each generation of human minds. As such it is like other human traits—for example, the control of fire, a trait that extends deep into the species' past and is found in every culture; it is universal because it provides things of value, like cooking, warmth, and light in the dark. Another example, according to Patel, is reading, another human invention built from existing brain systems, rather than resulting from an evolutionary modification of our brains. TTM theory posits that humans are drawn to music not, as discussed above, because they seek reward, but because of its "emotional power and efficacy for ritual and memory." As noted in the Introduction, Patel continues:

> *[G]rowing evidence from neuroscience . . . suggests that music is biologically powerful, meaning that it can have lasting effects on nonmusical abilities (such as language or attention) during the lifetime of individual humans. Importantly, these effects can be observed not only in trained musicians but also in ordinary individuals who engage regularly with music. Thus I believe that music should be regarded as a biologically powerful human invention or "transformative technology of the mind."[62]*

Contrary to Pinker's view that music is "biologically useless auditory cheesecake," TTM theory cites studies showing that engagement with music can result in lasting changes in nonmusical as well as musical brain functions. Regular engagement with music can exert lasting effects on brain functions in a wide range of individuals, such as improving cognitive abilities in children who are exposed to regular music lessons.[63] Music engages processing mechanisms shared with a wide range of cognitive domains, such as language, attention, auditory analysis, and social interaction.

Music may connect us to others. A recent study using fMRI and behavioral measures found evidence that, among higher-empathy people (there are ways of testing for that), music may be more than just a form of artistic expression: music is also about humans interacting with other humans and trying to understand and communicate with one another.[64] The results showed that music triggered the same complex social processes at work in the brain of high empathizers that are active during human social intercourse. The fMRI scans showed that these high empathizers experienced more activity in the dorsal striatum, part of the brain's reward system, when listening to music. In addition, scans also recorded greater activation in medial and lateral areas of the prefrontal cortex that are responsible for processing the social world, and in the temporoparietal junction, which is critical to analyzing and understanding others' behaviors and intentions. Typically, those areas of the brain are activated when people are interacting with, or thinking about, other people. Highly empathetic subjects—they studied graduate students—also seemed to experience a greater degree of pleasure in listening, as indicated by increased activation of the reward system. It's not correct to say that music causes one to be more empathetic, or more empathetic people choose to play or listen to music. The authors found a link, or correlation, not a cause and effect, but it doesn't hurt if educators, parents, philanthropists and politicians believe that it does! The more music in the world, the better for humanity!

When an esman (SS paramilitary guard) listened to music, especially of the kind he really liked, he somehow became strangely similar to a human being. His voice lost its typical harshness, he suddenly acquired an easy manner, and one could talk with him almost as one equal to another. Sometimes one got the impression that some melody stirred in him the memory of his dear ones, a girlfriend whom he had not seen for a long time, and then his eyes got misty with something that gave the illusion of human tears. At such moments the hope stirred in us that maybe everything was not lost after all. Could people who love music to this extent, people who can cry when they hear it, be at the same time capable of committing so many atrocities on the rest of humanity?

— Szymon Laks, conductor of an inmate orchestra at Auschwitz, in *Music of Another World*

2

WHY WE LIKE CERTAIN MUSIC
OR NONE AT ALL

A few years ago, I started a list in accordance with what Leonard Bernstein meant by "hardening of the categories."* Classical, pop, country-western, heavy metal, early, funk, grunge, cool jazz . . . The list kept growing as I sliced and diced music into what Apple now calls "genres," until I gave up. Maybe the old Schwann record catalogue started it (or just reflected it), but there is little question now that when we speak of "music," we are not all talking about the same thing.

Shakespeare had little uncertainty when he wrote, "If music be the food of love, play on." But by 1800, European concert programs reveal:

The growing popularity of songs and opera medleys, in some quarters, and the demand for more serious programming, in others, led to a breakdown of the old musical order . . . a change related to crises in national and international politics during the ensuing decades.[65]

By 1830, the phrase "classical music" had become widely accepted, and the classical repertory—the so-called canon—had begun to form. A division had opened up "along a spectrum of music deemed from light

* See Leonard Bernstein, *The Unanswered Question*

to serious," from music requiring only listening with "careless ease" to the music of "deceased great" (that is, "classical") composers—think Beethoven—requiring more serious effort, because it is music that makes art valuable, and serves as an "impetus to thought," in the words of a young critic cited by William Weber.[65] By the middle of the nineteenth century, the spectrum ran from the serious, or classical, concert, to the café or music hall concert, with "pops" or (in Britain) "Promenade" concerts somewhere in the middle.

Then blues music and later its more rowdy and gregarious sibling, jazz, burst out of the African-American communities of New Orleans as the twentieth century began.

> *Jazz speaks for life. The Blues tell the story of life's difficulties, and if you think for a moment, you will realize that they take the hardest realities of life and put them into music, only to come out with some new hope or sense of triumph.*
> –Martin Luther King, Jr., at the 1964 Berlin Jazz Festival

By the time George Gershwin paid a visit to Alban Berg in Vienna in 1928, he was sheepish about playing his own jazzy music for the eminent classical composer. Berg is said to have remarked: "Music, Mr. Gershwin, is music." For millennia that had been true, taking into account that music and dance usually went hand in hand: When you played or listened to music, you danced. You didn't sit passively in a chair amidst rows of other silent sitters to listen, unless you were at, say, a Russian church service, where the entire liturgy was sung by the clergy and a choir (see chapter 21). The nineteenth century saw the advent of the secular public concert and the separation of players from listeners, but only in the twentieth century did music fragment into dozens of "categories" (like species of ants or Protestants), which is still the case today. Some of our patrons at Gretna come for only one concert each summer: the one in their beloved category.

Alex Ross, with the help of ethnomusicologist Mark Slobin, theorizes on the genesis of our current "splintering of genres" that disturbed the older hierarchical division between "highbrow" and "lowbrow" and made it so difficult for Western classical music to maintain its balance in "this kaleidoscopic culture":

> *At some point during the lifetime of Richard Wagner, classical music overstepped the mark and turned megalomaniacal. Precisely because it advertised itself as universal, superior, and difficult, it stumbled badly in the new democratic marketplace. Jazz became the dominant form in the nineteen thirties and forties; rather quicker on its feet, it made a vibrant alliance with Tin Pan Alley while acquiring intellectual cachet by way of bebop. Then all genres had to bow before rock and roll, with its promise of global sexual and political liberation. But this revolution soon split apart as the more creative elements of punk and alternative rock renounced commercial values. Now nothing holds the center, and subcultures run amok.[66] See also Mark Slobin, Subcultural Sounds: Micromusics of the West (Hanover, NH: University Press of New England, 1993).*

What determines our preferred musical category or taste—the genres that you eventually choose to listen to? Or, the opposite: your choice to *not* listen to certain kinds of music? To start to answer those questions, I thought it would help to expand on a current model of "music in the brain" introduced in the previous chapter. It draws heavily on the work of hundreds of researchers, including two leaders in the field, both neurologists: Eckart Altenmüller at the University of Music, Drama and Media in Hanover, Lower Saxony, Germany, and Gottfried Schlaug at Harvard, who recently summarized many of the current concepts and experimental results.[67] Equally eminent psychologists are also working in a field that is exploding with interest and new discoveries.

As discussed above, in order to fully experience music, both the older, deep, "primitive" parts of the brain *and* the newer parts, especially the neocortex, which greatly expanded during the evolution of humans, must be called into action. The requirement of a highly developed neocortex probably explains why humans (*Homo sapiens*), with some exceptions, are the only species who play and listen to music. As for the former requirement, the older parts—like the amygdala, the nucleus accumbens, the hippocampus, and the midbrain—are critical for the emotional perception of music *and* also for our motivation to engage *in* music, a behavior—whether involving playing, listening, or both—that activates those same brain reward systems activated by sex, drugs, fine food and wine, religious ecstasy, sports, and probably other pleasures (to the degree to which you have grown to like them).

But, unlike as with sex, for example, activation of the old reward system by the new neocortex requires deliberate and systematic efforts to prepare or cultivate the networks in the neocortex. The ultimate success of that effort depends on the old nature vs. nurture conundrum: the degree to which the brain networks are already prepared at birth (native talent, also called "musicality"[68]) along with the intensity of the nurturing efforts to modify them (via practice and experience), thereby employing and guiding their "plasticity," after birth. One effect of recent research in "neuromusic," starting with Ericsson,[69] has been to dispel the myth that great artists are *only* those endowed with genes for musicality stemming from their birth into very musical families with amazing talent—and that talent alone, or even primarily, suffices for success as a musical artist. Instead, Ericsson showed that both innate talent and very hard work, beginning as early as possible in life, are necessary to develop into a world-class virtuoso in any field. And even when it comes to just *enjoying* music—that is, music alone, apart from the multi-sensory "productions" we experience at Super Bowl halftimes)—the more the effort, best expended early in life, the greater the reward.

Previous centuries offered us an older model of the brain: We are all born with a certain configuration of "hardware" in our brains, determined by our inherited DNA (genome) and already shaped to some degree by its environment in the womb. All "normal" human brains, according to this model, share the same recognizable basic anatomy: bilaterally symmetric shape and an almost identical pattern of convolutions (gyri, sulci, and fissures) divided into lobes—frontal, occipital, parietal, temporal; weighing about 1,300 grams (three pounds); containing the same components (eighty-six <u>b</u>illion nerve cells supported by a glial-cell framework and cables traveling through white matter and interconnecting layers of cells in the cortex [gray matter] and deeper lumps of gray matter called bodies and nuclei), that together make up the brain's 2 percent of body weight and consume 20 percent of the total calories used by the body. The components are served by a vascular system and cushioned by a cerebrospinal fluid system inside a protective bony skull.

In this old map of the brain, basic brain functions could be roughly localized:

• The left side of the cerebrum processes language, and senses and moves the right side of the body (and vice versa);

• Each occipital lobe in the back of the brain receives, and begins to process, images from the opposite half of the visual field;

• The pre-frontal lobe thinks, organizes, and executes;

• The frontal lobe handles movement, the parietal lobe sensation, and the temporal lobe sound and memory;

• The brainstem is a passageway for incoming and outgoing cables to the body and also a control panel for the cranial nerves, with wires to the eyes, face, ears, and throat;

• The cerebellum coordinates or fine-tunes much of the above activity.

(In this old model, the popular "left brain–right brain" dichotomy remains true to some degree—verbal abilities usually reside in the left hemisphere, spatial in the right—but the concept is a gross oversimplification, often misused. Would you say that Word and Photoshop are on different sides of your laptop?)

This basic brain map is derived from correlating observations of individuals who have suffered loss of particular brain functions (deficits), mostly from strokes, tumors, infections, and injuries, with the location of "lesions" (focal abnormalities or destruction) identified, in the late nineteenth and early twentieth centuries, by post-mortem examinations—and now from modern imaging techniques like computerized tomography (CT) and magnetic resonance imaging (MRI) in living patients.

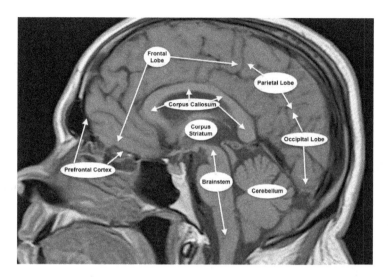

Figure 1. A sagittal section through the human brain "cut" by MRI in the same way a watermelon could be cut from front to back to reveal its seeds inside. Half of the nose, nasal cavity, lips, mouth and tongue can be seen on the left. Three lobes of the cerebrum can be seen, as can the cerebellum and brainstem. The temporal lobes that contain the amygdala, hippocampus, nucleus accumbens, and the auditory area, are not displayed by a sagittal section because they are on both sides of the cerebrum (one either side of this section). The human brain differs from that of all other species by having the largest cerebrum (frontal, parietal, and occipital lobes here, plus the temporal lobe) and thus the greatest area of cortex, the 2-4 mm mantle, called the neocortex in humans, that covers the surface of all the lobes like a tight sheet. That area is greatly increased by the ridges and groves (sulci and gyri), called convolutions, that appear here as the dark lines in the cerebrum. In the cerebellum the convolutions are best displayed by the "folia," the plant-like tufts at the top.

Medical textbooks explain the behavior of neurological diseases based upon where they attack the brain (or other elements of the nervous system, like the spine, the nerves, or muscles). Individual differences in disease behavior (from one stroke case to another, for example) arise more out of differences in the locations and size of the lesions and, because the basic anatomy of all normal human brains follows the same pattern, less from differences in the affected brains. So, for clinical diagnostic purposes, we assume that, in general, all human brains are very much alike.

As we advance beyond this older anatomical/structural model, functional imaging (fMRI) now can show activity in different locations as subjects perform specific mental or physical actions or experience external stimuli. We aren't surprised to see activity in particular anatomical regions while subjects perform or think about a particular task: Visual regions of the brain activate when subjects see something or just visualize it in their imagination; motor areas "light up" during movement, or even when the subject is just *thinking* of movement. By using music as one of those stimuli, we have greatly expanded such observations—because, as was discovered decades ago, playing and listening to music, as opposed to hearing simple sounds, activates a surprisingly large variety of different locations in both hemispheres of the brain. The brain "lights up" on an fMRI image when subjects listen to, imagine hearing (or hear in their mind's ear when reading a score), or even imagine playing music, a finding consistent with the pre-fMRI observation that music recruits the "'whole person' . . . cognitive, emotional, sensational, and behavioral at once."[70]

The common diagnostic MRI shows mainly the anatomy of the brain in greater detail than the older method of CT. CT employs radiation, MRI uses radio waves generated within a magnetic field.

A special MRI, called DTI (diffusion tensor imaging), can display structural integrity of small and large neuron pathways, or the "bandwidth" (like the diameter of a pipe) of "tracts" in white matter, that conduct electrical impulses like wires.

A functional MRI, fMRI, displays the amount of activity in particular locations in the brain (like a crowd gathering around an accident). Regions of greater activity "light up" when they are active and blood flow and glucose utilization increase to support the increased firing of nerve cells.

Such observations have led researchers to expand our concept of basic brain localization:[71]

• The frontal lobe is involved in the guidance of attention, in planning and motor preparation, in integrating auditory and motor information, and in specific human skills such as imitation and empathy. The two latter skills play an important role in the acquisition of musical skills and emotional expressiveness.

• Multisensory integration regions in the parietal lobe and temporo-occipital areas integrate different sensory inputs from the auditory, visual, and somatosensory system into a combined sensory impression; it is this multisensory brain representation which constitutes the typical musical experience.

• The cerebellum plays a critical role in musical experience. It is important for motor coordination and cognitive tasks, especially when they demand timing. Typically, the cerebellum is activated in rhythm processing, or tapping in synchrony with an external pacemaker such as a metronome.

An important change between the old and new models is that the new model accounts for differences we had been less attentive to in clinical diagnosis. These differences explain why, though all brains look alike and weigh about the same, the brain of every human who has ever walked on the planet has been unique. Underlying such differences are the microscopic components of the brain hardware and especially the billions of ways they can be interconnected in networks and circuits and affected by chemical transmitters. The "Human Connectome Project" is an ongoing, ever-expanding undertaking with the goal of mapping the brain's neural connections (numbering about 100 billion nerve cells times 100 trillion connectors) in their entirety. And note that NIH (National Institutes of Health) Director Francis S. Collins described the effort in a blog post titled "The Symphony inside Your Brain."[72]

Other new observations are equally interesting and instructive. Using new methods, we learned that repetitively performing mental or physical tasks can actually change the microscopic architecture and connectivity of the brain; that process activates a property of the brain called "plasticity" (more specifically, "neuroplasticity"). For example, we can show that after years of practice, a serious violinist may have, in his or her cerebral cortex (gray matter) in the right hemisphere of the brain, an area activated by use of the left (fingering) hand that has become larger than its counterpart region on the left. That area on the left activates the (right) hand holding the bow, a task requiring less complex finger motions.[73] Even the neglected "pinky" finger on the left (fingering) hand of a violinist finally gets a substantial area of cortical real estate! Musicians also have a larger cerebellum, correlating in degree with the intensity of their musical practice that calls for the cerebellum's role in motor coordination and rhythm.[74] Investigators tested music students at *Hochschule für Musik* (College or Conservatory for Music) in Basel before and after they underwent two semesters of intensive ear training. After the training, they found (by means of fMRI) that functioning in a critical region in the brain called the hippocampus had enlarged, presumably to build more capacity for musical memory.[75]

Observations of "musical" brain characteristics have extended from measuring the size of locations activated by music in the brain to determining the extent and strength of connections *among* locations. In general, the connectors are white matter and sometimes called tracts or fascicles. They connect groups of brain nerve cells (neurons) with other groups, also called nuclei, or with the sheets of neurons in the cerebral cortex. The groups and sheets are called gray matter and most of the groups have names like "striate nucleus" or thalamus. The cortex is named according to the lobe of the brain it covers, like the temporal or frontal lobe. A pianist may possess a larger than average white-matter connector between the left and right hemispheres called the *corpus callosum*, because of the need to coordinate and integrate the actions of both hands.[76] (It is difficult to imagine any musical activity more complex and demanding than that required to play the Rachmaninoff *Third Piano Concerto*! Both hemispheres of the brain must work together precisely and at full steam.) Long-term vocal training can increase the volume and complexity of the *arcuate fasciclus*, composed of white matter tracts connecting the temporal and frontal lobes. Both of those lobes are fundamental to sound perception and production, and to its feedforward and feedback control, the ability to hear your voice and make instant necessary adjustments to it. The larger fascicles in singers can even be distinguished from those of instrumentalists, though the latter must also make the same continuous corrections to their sound.[77]

Although, in general, the brain pathways for music are parallel to those for language, we are beginning to identify cells and networks dedicated exclusively to music. MIT investigators found a neural population in the human auditory cortex, the brain's reception room in the temporal lobe for all sounds, that responds only to music—not to speech or other environmental sounds.[78]

These newer observations have begun to reveal possible reasons for individual brain differences—not only among humans in general, but also between musicians and non-musicians and *among* musicians— thereby starting us along the way to understanding why each human is unique and why we each possess certain preferences, including those for certain kinds of music. Underlying these differences are differences in connectivity—that is, differences in how all the locations in the brain are connected or wired together, as well as in the number, complexity, and length of the connections. In other words, we start to consider the brain as a network—like a computer, an electrical grid, or the aggregate of corporations required to build a jet airliner. There are different kinds of brain networks, depending on how the components are interconnected. Many brain networks are "small world" networks, in which innumerable large and small nodes or centers are connected both to each other and to nearby and distant large and small nodes.

♫

We can begin to think, now, about the consequences of the varying strengths of the connections—between "hyperconnection" at one extreme and "disconnection" at the other—between locations in the brain.

An extreme example is the first clinical "disconnection syndrome," described in 1874 by the neurologist Carl Wernicke. The disconnection occurs, often because of a stroke, between the "auditory center" in the left temporal lobe, where speech is received and processed, and the "speech center" nearby in the left frontal lobe, from which propositional speech is sent to the "telegraph office" for dispatch by the vocal cords, lips, and tongue.[79] (We now label that auditory center "Wernicke's area" of cortex and the speech center Broca's area.) That disconnection causes "conduction aphasia": The victim can understand language and also initiate propositional speech—that is, speech containing meaningful words and significant information, as opposed to memorized or "by rote" speech—but cannot "repeat after me" anything spoken to him. Input has been disconnected from output. An interesting recent discovery is that one cause of unconsciousness may be a lesion in the brainstem (say from a stroke or a boxing match) that disconnects two regions in the cerebral cortex, one or both of which are necessary for normal wakefulness.[80]

You would be correct, therefore, in thinking that the initial, inborn configuration of our brain networks, with its centers and connections, determines to a large degree who we are, what we like, our temperament, our potential, and other qualities that make each of us unique. Peculiarities in our inborn networks are considered likely to account for certain "neurodevelopmental" disorders characterized by deficiencies in certain abilities or qualities, as in autism, dyslexia, stuttering, and, importantly for this discussion, amusia (the inability to distinguish music from other sounds) and musical anhedonia. Other qualities, such as exceptional skills in music or genius in mathematics, could relate to especially strong ("hyper") connectivity in certain parts of our networks. "Savant"-like abilities, or Asperger's syndrome on the autism spectrum, probably relate to combinations of unusually strong connections combined with (or at the expense of) other unusually weak ones. In almost all such instances, because the peculiarities affect only "connectivity," standard diagnostic scans—MRIs or CTs—show no trace of the causes, because the basic, "macroscopic" anatomical structure of the brain is "normal."

Another example of hyperconnectivity may be synesthesia, a trait far more common among artists and poets.* One form of synesthesia is seeing or imagining music in colors, which may be caused by especially strong connections between auditory and visual regions in the brain.[81] The pianist Hélène Grimaud observed that

> *each tonality has a color that represents it, and so the main color dominating the piece is going to be the color of the tonality in which the piece is written and, of course, with every modulation it will change. What I find interesting is that it brings us back to this idea from the Baroque times about how every tonality has its own emotional identity in a way, that they are not even-tempered [chapter 10 is a discussion of temperament] even if they are equivalent. I've described it as something like the byproduct of an altered sense of perception. I think it takes place if you're exposed to something as powerful as music.[82]*

A recent study from researchers at three European institutes has, for the first time, identified specific genes that are linked to sound-color synesthesia in multiple relatives of three families across at least three generations.[84] The genes relate to axonogenesis (formation of nerve transmitting wires called axons), possibly connecting brain areas usually segregated from one another, such as the color-selective region and the auditory region.

One advantage of synesthesia may be an enhanced ability to memorize. For a simple example, imagine that you walk onto the stage and can't remember the note that begins the next work on the program. If, however, you associate a color with the piece, you might have a better chance to start it on the right note – or to remember how to transition to the development section if you think of that in color.

* Shakespeare's Romeo, "It is the East, and Juliet is the sun." Isaac Newton who knew about sound waves may have postulated that light travels in a spectrum of waves because he may have had synesthesia. He made a toy musical instrument which would flash colors corresponding to tones.[83]

Perfect, or absolute pitch (AP), is yet another quality associated with hyperconnectivity. In the summer of 1763, just before the Mozart family embarked on the famous tour of Europe that established the young composer's reputation as a musical prodigy, an anonymous letter appeared in the *Augsburgischer Intelligenz-Zettel*, describing seven-year-old Wolfgang's extraordinary abilities:

> *Furthermore, I saw and heard how, when he was made to listen in another room, they would give him notes, now high, now low, not only on the pianoforte but on every other imaginable instrument as well, and he came out with the letter of the name of the note in an instant. Indeed, on hearing a bell toll, or a clock or even a pocket watch strike, he was able at the same moment to name the note of the bell or time piece.*[85]

In most cases, AP can be gained by training (deliberate or otherwise) only early in the first decade of life.[86] But not all humans may be genetically capable of acquiring this ability, possibly because they were born with very few—or a total lack—of the necessary brain white-matter connections, so that no amount of effort can increase them. In humans with AP (somewhere between one in one thousand and one in ten thousand, more prevalent in countries with tone languages in Asia[87]), the ability is usually apparent by the age of ten; such people have the ability to identify a note in the absence of any references or clues. We test for AP in the laboratory by asking subjects to identify a single pure tone—say, middle C—produced electronically so that it has no overtones, such as the overtones that enable almost anyone to distinguish a flute (mostly even overtones) from an oboe (odd overtones). A person with AP would, like Mozart, correctly and immediately identify a tone produced by *any* source or instrument with a frequency of 440 Hertz (Hz, vibrations per second) as the note A. (Plasticity also accounts for the fact that two centuries ago, listeners expected and were quite satisfied when A was 226 Hz, though it has gradually increased to 440, sometimes even higher, since then.)

I could always name a note produced on my mother's piano, using the clues provided by the unique quality of each of the notes that she and I played a lot during my childhood. Similarly, I am better at identifying notes played by a flute after a lifetime of playing them, because each note has a unique quality (i.e., set of overtones recognized best by flutists) that provides a clue. Another "hint" that would make it easier for a musician to identify notes in a composition would be knowing that the piece is in a particular key. But I failed in the laboratory to correctly name pure tones. Alas, I don't have AP, probably because I started piano lessons relatively late, at the age of eight years.

But I do (I think) have good "relative pitch," as should most musicians (at least those with "good ears" fine-tuned by experience or, if necessary, by "ear training"—whether or not it is called that—by a good music teacher or in a conservatory class). Once any given note is identified, then I can correctly identify other notes by their relationship to it. In other words, good musicians can recognize intervals (the pitch differences between two notes)—major or minor thirds, fifths, and all other intervals—and thus can name each note in any scale if they know any one pitch. (That ability is not the same as, but is related to, the ability to sing or play notes "on pitch"—that is, precisely identical to the pitch of the notes played by others in an ensemble—and accurately within the "temperament" of the scale that all others in the ensemble are using.)

Hearing intervals (differences between notes) is exactly the ability lacking in the small percentage of humans with amusia, also called tone deafness—especially those born with that problem.[88] (Acquired amusia is a more heterogeneous condition because it can result from diverse diseases such as stroke, brain injury, or dementia. Oliver Sacks describes his own temporary amusia during a migraine.[89]) Not only can amusics not identify any intervals; they can't tell whether any given note is higher or lower than another or different from another or if that difference is changing, unless the difference or the changes are very large. They can't hear small differences in pitch—say, if a soprano is singing flat. Observations tell us that about 5 percent of humans have that inability,[90] but like all human traits, it occurs in varying degrees. Concordance among twins suggests a familial genetic component.[91]

Recent studies have begun to reveal specific connectivity differences in the brain associated with AP and amusia and suggest that they are related—or more specifically, occupy opposite ends of a spectrum. Those with AP have structural and functional hyperconnectivity through a larger-than-average white matter connector cable that links the left superior temporal gyrus—gray matter in the temporal lobe—to the left middle temporal gyrus, a neighboring area of gray matter.[92] Not surprisingly, 20 percent of individuals with AP also have synesthesia, another trait linked to hyperconnectivity.[93]

In contrast, musically tone-deaf individuals have reduced (hypo-) connectivity compared with musically normal-functioning individuals, in their case through the connector cable—from temporal to frontal lobe—a curved white-matter tract called the arcuate fasciculus. In clinical speak, this phenomenon, which parallels "disconnection aphasia" (described above), could be called an inborn "disconnection syndrome." That's not surprising to those who have begun to consider music a "paralinguistic" process. In light of the possibility that dyslexia and tone deafness have a shared, similar, and/or common neural basis, we might explore the potential for musical treatments for aphasia and dyslexia. Singing has already been employed in the treatment of stroke patients who have aphasia. Is it not too far of a leap to speculate whether it might be worthwhile to try to train every child to acquire perfect pitch, because that skill might be transferable in later life to enhance linguistic ability!

Not surprisingly, both AP and amusia vary in degree, so we can consider individual cases along a spectrum, just as we consider autism. (That concept, of course, does not account for the fact that each individual with autism differs in innumerable ways—along other axes, so to speak—but applying some measure of severity is a useful way of estimating the chances of each individual's learning skills of living or functioning in society.) When testing for AP, for example, we find some people who are always (100 percent or very close) accurate in identifying the correct pitch, others who are *mostly* accurate (that is, to varying degrees better than chance), and still others who are accurate only at the rate that would be predicted *by* chance. We might speculate that the degree of accuracy might relate to the connective strength (i.e., bandwidth) of the arcuate fasciculus—its overall size, or the integrity of its individual fascicles as shown by DTI (a particular kind of MRI that reveals the integrity of connections). Similarly, the degree (or "severity," if you wish) of amusia can be quantified as the size of the difference in pitch necessary for an amusic person to detect that difference—those with the greatest degree of amusia needing a large difference to detect that two notes are not the same pitch.

It has been questioned, partly because of the case of Mozart, whether AP is associated with any degree of exceptional musicality, musical memory, or ability to perform, but the evidence is unclear. Whether other eminent composers and musicians in the past had AP was not established as definitely as it was in the case of Mozart—because they were not tested. On the one hand, AP is clearly *not* a necessary quality for excellence in musicianship; musicians as eminent as Stravinsky lacked it. On the other hand, far more accomplished musicians—up to as many as 20 percent—have AP than members of the general public.

Finally, consider the concept of a broader spectrum on which humans with AP and those with amusia occupy opposite ends: We might call them the "very musical" and "not at all musical" ends, respectively. Humans near the AP end of this spectrum, by virtue of possessing the ability to more acutely perceive small differences in pitch from birth, could experience rewards from listening to and playing music during their early periods of increased plasticity (see chapter 3), while those near the amusical end, endowed with minimal ability to hear or understand music, had little incentive to listen to music during their critical periods and thus never strengthened their connections between their "old" and "new" brains, thereby linking music to their pleasure networks.

The majority of humans probably fall somewhere in the "moderately musical" center of this broad spectrum: They respond to relatively simple melodies, harmonies, and rhythms (called "popular" music for obvious reasons), listen casually or passively, but do not learn to play music during critical developmental periods; they then find what we might call a "comfortable familiarity" (in my view, a relatively low level of reward from music) with that same music later in life. They have a casual interest in music and attend concerts of simpler and less complex music, much as they are attracted to sports events and other forms of entertainment requiring an average degree of education and life experience. The AP end includes humans who have attained the connectivity necessary to respond with pleasure to the complex music of Mahler or Debussy; at the amusical end are those who don't hear or comprehend any music at all.

So another strong determinant of your musical "category" (*a la* Bernstein) is *when* you grew up, or to put it another way, the schedule in your life when your brain plasticity was most strongly influenced by playing or hearing music. (See the discussion of "critical" and "sensitive" periods for acquisition of musical skills in the next chapter.) We can predict the average age of the audience at Gretna Theater's "retrospectives," which feature cover bands (who play arrangements of older popular artists, some who have passed away) playing music of the 1940s, '50s, or '60s, because, according to musician/psychologist Dan Levitin:

> *Fourteen is a sort of magic age for the development of musical tastes. You're in the ninth grade, confronting the tyrannies of sex and adulthood, struggling to figure out what kind of adult you'd like to be, and you turn to the cultural products most important in your day as sources of cool—the capital of young life. Musical tastes become a badge of identity in social contexts framed by pop culture.*[94]

That colorful idea may of course be an oversimplification of a very complex issue discussed in detail in *JAMA* almost two decades ago. Quoting anthropologist A. P. Merriam in *The Anthropology of Music*, who wrote about the tremendous power of music as "so all-pervasive [that it] reaches into, shapes and often controls so much of human behavior," the authors of that *JAMA* article view music as a communicative force that affects attitude, mood, emotions, and behavior. All of these qualities are in turmoil and conflict during adolescence, a critical period for many areas of development:

> *During adolescence, teenagers are expected to develop stan-*
> *dards of behavior and reconcile them with their perceptions of*
> *adult standards. In this context, music, a powerful medium in*
> *the lives of adolescents, offers conflicting values. The explicit*
> *sexual and violent lyrics of some forms of music often clash*
> *with the themes of abstinence and rational behavior promoted*
> *by adult society. Identification with rock music, particularly*
> *those styles that are rejected by adults, functions to separate*
> *adolescents from adult society. Some forms of rock music extend*
> *well beyond respectability in fulfilling this definitional role.*
> *Total immersion into a rock subculture, such as heavy met-*
> *al, may be both a portrait of adolescent alienation and*
> *an unflattering reflection of an adolescent's perception of the*
> *moral and ethical duplicity of adult society.[95]*

The authors' call for physicians to be "aware of the role of music in the lives of adolescents and use music preferences as clues to the emotional and mental health of adolescents" may seem futile as well as quaint, given the directions health care has taken since then.

That age, around fourteen, also seems to be when our brain is most receptive to form perceptual templates that set our expectations for each time we hear temporal (rhythmic), harmonic, and pitch patterns of sound from then on. I haven't fully investigated the science backing that assertion, but it held true for me, though I don't recall feeling very alienated in the 1950s. As a child, I had raced through categories. At home sick from first grade, I called in a request to a local AM radio station for a gospel song, "Up Above My Head," that I liked to hear over and over, perhaps because of the passion and joy of the choir. A few years later, I marched to the rhythm of the Cities Service Band of America every Monday night, after we finally got FM radio. A year or two later, I liked broadcasts of Marian McPartland and the Oklahoma City Symphony, along with the Boston Pops and Leroy Anderson. Now I wish my parents had listened to the Metropolitan Opera on Saturday afternoons.

At about age fourteen, after having heard my father play his collection of heavy, fragile 78s [rpm] since I had learned to walk, I feasted on the sounds of Schubert, Beethoven, Stravinsky, and Sibelius. These were his badges of identity, and thus became mine. An identity like his was my goal.

Charles Rosen mentions an interesting additional factor that may apply to those of us experiencing our sensitive periods for music during "the time that listening to records was beginning to overtake going to concerts as the chief way of staying in contact with the classical tradition. . . the record companies consistently refused to make records freely or cheaply available to schools."[96] That was the era when a 45 rpm single, usually of a pop tune, was less expensive than an LP (long-playing) 33 rpm classical album. Perhaps that was the point at which the pump of classical listeners lost (forever?) its priming.

So "why we like certain music" boils down to 1) the strength of our innate endowment, which determines our potential and limits, and 2) the way that endowment is nurtured at a time of critical brain plasticity in our lives.

A recent study takes us closer to parsing these effects, at least with respect to Western music. It asked: "Do our inborn hardware connections determine what we hear as pleasant?" Do biological reasons, for example, account for the fact that we all hear a major triad as pleasant (consonant), and a tritone, or two adjacent notes on a piano, as unpleasant (dissonant)? After all, Pythagoras showed that there is a physical basis for the notes of a scale: You can blow only consonant notes on a valveless horn and produce only consonant notes by stopping a vibrating string at halves, thirds, and fifths. Investigators at MIT and Brandeis found that members of a native Amazonian society, the Tsimané, isolated from Western music though having normal auditory perceptive abilities, heard consonant and dissonant chords and vocal harmonies as equally pleasant. Bolivian city-dwellers, in contrast, had the same preference for consonance as we do, suggesting that "culture has a dominant role in shaping aesthetic responses to music."[97] (The Tsimané are also remarkably free of coronary atherosclerotic disease—or will be until they discover Big Macs and fries.)[98]

Millennials may speak of "my music." If it fits into a category (or "genre" on iTunes), they may not know exactly which, but they can easily find the most popular sources of "cool" in any particular window of time in their lives. Even if they have musical anhedonia (they don't get pleasure from music), they still might add that music to their badge of identity. Hearing those songs from childhood and teenage years later in life, they can respond to their familiarity and the associations they trigger with the past. Alas, if they avoid the more complex classical genre ("old music"), as do some parents, schools, and even churches now, they may have a limited repertoire of pleasures to call upon in maturity. Like arteries, musical categories start hardening early in life. Attempting to keep my categories and arteries open, I have been amply rewarded by "new" (to me) music written in all eras over many hundreds of years, including my own lifetime.

Sing – Sing a song
Make it simple
To last your whole life long
Don't worry that
it's not good enough
For anyone else to hear
Sing – Sing a song
— "Sing," by Joe Raposo

Sing God a simple song
Lauda, Laudē
Make it up as you go along
Lauda, Laudē
Sing like you like to sing;
God loves all simple things
For God is the simplest of all.
— "A Simple Song," by Leonard Bernstein

3

CAN LEARNING MUSIC MAKE US SMARTER?

Singing or playing music calls many parts of the brain into action, activating millions of components, circuits, and networks in the cerebrum, brainstem, and cerebellum.

When I play the flute, I call upon vision, to read and interpret a complex printed code on a music stand. I need fine sensorimotor control, to sense the keys under my fingers and command my fingers to press, in milliseconds, multiple combinations of those keys. I listen critically, in order to instantly match my sounds to those of other players in the ensemble. I call up memory, to remember phrases of the piece I am playing stored in my brain's bookshelf. I require coordination, between my tongue and both hands, to fit my playing precisely into a tempo, either that of the others in the ensemble or the imaginary, or "entrained," beat going in my brain. I have learned deep-breathing and breath control techniques, and how to vary my breath according to the intensity of a given phrase so that it will last for the length of that phrase. I employ expressiveness and emotion, so that my phrasing, dynamics, and style, layered onto the sounds I produce, will fit the character and sense of the composition. I evaluate my own sounds—with respect to pitch, tone quality, pace, tempo, and compatibility with the ensemble—in a feedback loop that enables constant corrections vis-à-vis all of the functions mentioned above as needed.

And all of these abilities are put into the service of communicating with listeners. All instruments and singing demand similar abilities and more.

Eminent researchers describe music playing and listening similarly:

> *[M]usic is one of the richest human emotional, sensory-motor, and cognitive experiences. It involves listening, watching, feeling, moving and coordinating, remembering, and expecting musical elements. It is frequently accompanied by strong emotions resulting in joy, happiness, and bittersweet sadness or even in overwhelming bodily reactions like tears in the eyes or shivers down the spine. A large number of cortical and subcortical brain regions are involved in music listening and music making activities.*[99]

Every time it is undertaken, that effort and activity, in practice or performance—some of it conscious, some unconscious, much of it "automatic"—not only activates the brain but also makes changes in the brain—some temporary, some permanent—in specific locations, connections, and networks. Practice is the controlled and deliberate way by which I can effect these changes—even, thankfully, still at my "certain" age. And the brain's plasticity enables it to adapt and change in response to my demands. Though the term "plasticity" may seem new, scientists, and especially musicians, have known for millennia that practice leads to changes in performance—what we call improvement. But only during my career have we realized that the brain itself actually creates new elements—cells, connections, networks—throughout life. Musicians of the current generation, responding to intense competition and seeking perfection, have carried this phenomenon to its greatest extreme ever. (Perhaps we can suspect a few historic exceptions, such as Franz Liszt or Paganini, but we have no recordings to confirm those suspicions.)

Of course, all learning, on some level, requires plasticity. A two-year-old's first conscious experience with the phenomenon of plasticity may be learning to sing "Mary Had a Little Lamb." Oblivious to the chemical, physical, and electrical changes in his or her brain, a child can nevertheless memorize different pitch intervals as well as rhythm and language, among other skills. After several coached repetitions—"Try again"—most children can sing the song alone or sing it with another person. They also learn that they *can* learn.

Memorizing in music is sometimes called "muscle memory" or "motor learning"—two ways of expressing what is also called "procedural memory," which involves consolidating a specific motor task into memory through repetition. In my case, I don't say during a morning of practice that I want to memorize any particular passage of music. Instead, I practice an entire movement or passage repetitively, day after day, until I can walk away from the printed notes on the music stand and play them accurately and reliably. I suspect most musicians would say the same, but they can't apply it to everything they play, especially when they must play different music every day. A corollary, at least for me, is that if I can't play an important passage or solo work of music from memory, I don't feel I have learned it completely. By learning it completely I mean that I can automatically play it, almost without thinking about what notes come next, and that I can totally attend to converting the notes into music that speaks to my listeners. A vexing feature of this kind of memory, however, is that if memory fails at some point in the middle of a passage, I often must return to the beginning—of that passage or of the entire piece—because I can't always resume from the point of failure.

Learning in the brain is probably first enabled by increases in the number of packets of chemical transmitters that carry messages across a gap or synapse from one nerve cell (neuron) to another in the circuits of nerve cells used in any particular learning task.[100] After a day, or perhaps several days, of coaching and repetition, the brain begins to build anatomical changes to those same parts and pathways—almost but not quite like replacing a ferry across a river by a bridge. This biological building process probably includes growing more dendritic spines (microscopic connections, like twigs on a branch), more and larger synapses (contacts between one nerve cell and another), actual nerve cells, and other supportive hardware that together forms complex networks that will ultimately contain, in the entire brain, more than one hundred billion neurons (cells) and one hundred trillion connections among the cells that transmit electrical signals throughout the brain.[101] Through countless similar learning incidents, each young brain is gradually built in a unique way, determined by the totality and characteristics of the experiences unique to each of us.

More formally put: Neural plasticity—changes in brain structure and function—underlies development, learning, skill refinement, and rehabilitation from trauma.[102] The degree of these changes correlates with the duration and intensity of practice. Enlarging or strengthening parts of your brain by means of intense practice of any activity can be a good way to spend your time—and the examples above and in chapter 2 illustrate just a few among the millions of changes, especially in the brain's auditory and motor areas, enabled by repetitive activation and plasticity during music making.[103] And evidence is accumulating that the brain hardware expanded by musical practice may be available for later use in performing other tasks, enabling musical skills to be transferred to other skills.

Plasticity persists as a brain property throughout a lifetime—I can still learn to play and memorize new music—but the human brain is most plastic with respect to music and several other skills during the first decade or two of life. Then the plasticity for acquisition of some skills begins to diminish. Certain brain abilities can be gained only at certain ages, called "critical periods": In such cases, the opportunity opens up only once during life, when cerebral cortical plasticity is maximum, and then closes tightly and permanently.

A good example of a critical period involves acquiring the ability to integrate two slightly different images, one from each eye, in order to enable true binocular stereoscopic (3-D) vision. When, from birth, the eyes are not precisely focused on the same point (crossed eyes or wall eyes, both forms of the condition called "strabismus"), then the resulting double vision requires a child to unconsciously suppress one of the two images. If the eyes are not aligned (by surgery, exercises, refractive correction, or occasionally via normal development) before the age of six or seven years, then the critical period for acquiring normal binocular vision and depth perception ends, and such vision will never be possible, even if the eyes are perfectly aligned later in life.[104] If one eye is consistently not used (its vision unconsciously suppressed) during that critical period, it never develops normal sight (and becomes a "lazy" eye), though if forced into use in adult life—say, if the other eye fails—its vision can improve to a limited degree.

We also recognize other sensitive periods in development.[105] Children are very sensitive to learning languages during their first decade—so sensitive that in bilingual households they can even learn more than one language simultaneously. If they learn several languages—almost effortlessly if they hear them spoken regularly—before they reach the age of eleven, they will usually acquire the lifelong ability to speak each of them, and without an accent.[106] After about age eleven, the language learning process becomes increasingly more difficult, taking more time and effort, and an accent when speaking a non-native tongue is almost inevitable.

There is a similar sensitive period for learning music—which, accounting for individual variations of a few years, is most robust during the first decade of life, somewhat less during the second, and even less after that.[107] These periods are similar to those for acquiring certain other skills, such as swimming, bicycle riding, and skiing. One of the most interesting skills to consider is improvisation. The younger we are, the more our actions are improvisatory, because we have never done them before. According to Vijay Iyer, an improviser on the piano at the level of Art Tatum, "improvisation, whether artistic, social, or cultural, as in the manner of a diaspora, involves the ability to perceive, think, decide, and act in real time."[108] It is how we learn to do everything: how we learn to talk, to walk, and to eat: "We tend to think of improvisation, especially in the West, as some sort of extreme occasion. But it's sort of a banal thing that we always do. . . . " In Iyer's view, traditional music education suppresses the ability to improvise by replacing it with the strict "rules and regulations" required to reproduce a written musical score exactly as it was written by the composer. Shunryu Suzuki, founding Abbott of the San Francisco Zen Center, expressed the same thought more succinctly: "In the beginner's mind there are many possibilities, but in the expert's mind there are few."[109]

We can all learn basic musical skills later in life; but by then, because of far less plasticity, we have little chance of excelling in any of them, let alone becoming a professional musician. But the skills gained early during sensitive periods, like bicycle riding, are deeply imprinted. I didn't ride a bicycle between the ages of eighteen and sixty-five, but when I started again in retirement, that skill had been undiminished over almost fifty years. So if you want to become a professional musician, skier, tennis player, or the like, your abilities, or most of them, had better be hardwired in your brain (and to a lesser extent, in your body) by the age of twenty; otherwise, your best hope is to become a talented amateur. More complex characteristics or abilities—say, empathy or kindness—may need to await the maturity of later life. The Dalai Lama raised an interesting possibility: that meditation is another way to effect changes in brain structure and function. He and others have said that learning about neuroplasticity increased their motivation to practice meditation.[110]

Even before we began to use the word "plasticity," Ericsson et al. had explored the concept in an extremely thorough and well-documented study and review in 1993.[111] His conclusion has become an almost pedagogical law in music albeit sometimes distorted and misunderstood when passed along in casual conversations and publications (like this one). It may not accurately apply, for example, to the Beatles' many hours of pub performances. The law (in my humble interpretation) holds that given adequate innate mental and physical prerequisites (so that you can't become a professional basketball player if you are only five feet tall, or a professional violinist if you have a hearing disability from birth), those who become the very best soloists or professional violinists and pianists, as opposed to good amateurs or teachers, begin at the earliest age (before five years), and then must accumulate, by about the age of twenty, ten thousand hours of

> deliberate practice . . . a specific type of music-related activity, which is judged to be most relevant for improvement of music performance, effortful, and less inherently enjoyable than leisure and several other music-related activities.[112]

Such intensity of practice typically averages about twenty hours a week. The practice should be thoughtful, systematic, and professionally guided. For comparison, the researchers estimated that most violinists sitting in the sections of major orchestras accumulated on average about seven thousand to eight thousand hours of such practice; an average amateur pianist probably logs about fifteen hundred hours. These rigorous time requirements may be less for players of less complex repertoire and instruments, like the trumpet or oboe, but knowing the exact numbers would require a similar study on each group of instruments. Ericsson et al. remark further:

> *We agree that expert performance is qualitatively different from normal performance, and even that expert performers have characteristics and abilities that are qualitatively different from or at least outside the range of those of normal adults. However, we deny that these differences are immutable, that is, due to innate talent. Only a few exceptions, most notably height, are genetically prescribed. Instead, we argue that the differences between expert performers and normal adults reflect a lifelong period of deliberate effort to improve performance in a specific domain.*[113]

Gray matter cell density and connectivity, most plastic in early decades, continues to be plastic to a lesser degree indefinitely. White matter tracts probably continue developing until the age of thirty; their volume and effectiveness have been linked to cognitive as well as performance skills. Now there is evidence (so far only in mice) that a switch—a protein called the "Nogo Receptor" —may gradually (unlike a light switch) suppress plasticity after adolescence, in order to stabilize or hardwire the brain for life.[114] That concept is sometimes called "pruning."

Fortunately, acquisition of other abilities (as well as knowledge and wisdom) is still open to the older brain (meaning, older than twenty years). After your ten thousand hours of musical practice by late adolescence, you can go to college at Harvard (like Yo-Yo Ma) and to graduate or professional school, and expect to become a doctor, professor, scientist, or business person, so long (it seems fair to speculate) as you have acquired beforehand necessary basic learning skills (say those in the medieval university's *trivium and quadrivium*: grammar, rhetoric, and logic; arithmetic, geometry, astronomy, and music.) So what I'm saying here isn't anything really new. During the course of your ten thousand hours of practicing your instrument and attending school, you are likely to acquire most, if not all, of those critical basic faculties—and to learn how to learn. Then the brain, having been disciplined early, can still accumulate information, knowledge, and hopefully wisdom at a more measured pace throughout life. (As Thomas Jefferson instructed his daughter, Patsy: "With respect to the distribution of your time, the following is what I should approve: From 8 to 10, practice music. . . .") (More on Jefferson, chapter 26.) At that rate, Patsy (if she is a very obedient daughter) would have logged about five thousand hours over ten years. You can't follow that schedule in reverse, however. Late-starting tennis players and pianists are forever amateurs: playing for their own enjoyment, rarely for ticket buyers. There is a difference between a child who starts to play the piano at age five to six and diligently practices, and another who decides to imitate a pianist he or she hears on YouTube at age fourteen.

I found the technical aspects of music making (at least on the flute, though not on the piano) relatively easy, so that by age twenty I could effortlessly play just about anything, regardless of its technical demands. What I lacked, however (being many hours short of ten thousand), was the elusive quality of musicality that would have enhanced my ability to communicate, or effectively express, the music to listeners—an ability that, I suspect, comes with hearing lots of music and gaining lots of life experience. I hesitate to imagine what listeners might have been thinking during one of my hour-long solo performances. Only a lifetime's experience, musical and otherwise, has allowed me to (sometimes, maybe) play music rather than notes. And I still prefer solo performances by violinists and pianists; their instruments permit a wider range of expressivity than does the flute—and thus require the investment of many more hours of practice. To reach the same level of musical ability starting later in life (that is, after age twenty, and assuming it is possible at all) would certainly require far more than ten thousand hours.

In one sense, the mission of an orchestra conductor, among many (such as keeping ninety players playing together), is to bestow his or her ten thousand hours of musicality upon players who may not all have completed their then thousand hours—though some of a conductor's hours may have been logged earlier in her career, in piano, violin, or even oboe practice.

A vital question, still not completely answered, is the extent to which we can transfer musical abilities and skills acquired in childhood—like playing the piano—to other abilities later in life. Research suggests that young musicians, for example, may develop better language skills, executive functions, working memory, perceptual speed, auditory and motor skills, and more. Studies have concluded that musically educated kids do better in school, exhibiting stronger reading skills, increased math abilities, and higher general intelligence scores.[115] Music even seems to improve social development, as children begin to find that music helps them be better team players and have higher self-esteem. (Take that, football coaches.) "Based on what we already know about the ways that music helps shape the brain," notes Dr. Nina Kraus of the Auditory Neuroscience Laboratory at Northwestern University, "our study suggests that short-term music lessons may enhance lifelong listening and learning."[116] Quoted in *Scientific American*, Dr. Kraus said: "To learn to read, you need to have good working memory, the ability to disambiguate speech sounds, [and the ability to] make sound-to-meaning connections. Each one of these things really seems to be strengthened with active engagement in playing a musical instrument."[117]

In a recent review of current knowledge, Kraus concluded that music training "augments the neural processing of speech," and probably even enhances understanding when reading. It improves the ability to "make sense of speech in complex, everyday listening environments," such as in a noisy restaurant, or in other places where there is background noise. Kraus feels that listening and language skills are "biologically intertwined."[118]

In one study, "Neurobiology of Everyday Communication," Kraus and researchers collaborated with Harmony Project (www.harmony-project.org), a Los Angeles–based music and mentorship program that has provided free music instruction to more than one thousand children from gang-reduction zones in the city. The study randomly assigned children (ages six to nine) to either a music instruction group or to a waitlist (serving as a short-term control group), with guaranteed admission to music training the following year. By the study's conclusion, the music training improved the ability of the instructed group to perceive speech in a noisy environment and showed neurophysiological evidence of improved language processing and literacy skills. Kraus and White-Schwoch cite a host of related studies in a comprehensive review.[119]

Investigators in Canada and Hong Kong studied two groups of seven- and eight-year-old children (thirty-seven boys, thirty-six girls).[120] One group took music lessons, the other "enhanced education in mathematics and general studies." A third group of twenty-three received no additional instruction. After eighteen months, the children in the music group showed a greater increase on every measure of verbal memory than those in the other two groups (after adjustment for influences of IQ and age). The researchers postulated that "playing music requires continued monitoring of meaningful chunks of information . . . Rather than individual notes, these chunks entail clusters of notes that are combined into meaningful melodic gestures and phrases."

♫

Executive functions (EF) are cognitive capacities that enable planned, controlled behavior and strongly correlate with academic abilities. And another study suggests that musically trained children have significantly greater brain activation (as assessed by fMRI) in traditional EF regions when switching from one task to another, and perform better on measures of verbal fluency and processing speed. The investigators argue that the results support links between musical training and enhanced cognitive skills and academic achievement.[121]

But do those results and others show only *correlation*—of early musical training with higher intelligence—but not causation? Do they mean that early musical education results in higher general intelligence or non-musical achievement later in life? Invoking causation certainly serves the goals of the music education field and of advocates for more funding for it—not to mention those of us who plead for more people to buy tickets to concerts. A group of Canadian investigators, based on their results over several years, have suspected widespread bias in interpreting correlational data as evidence that music training causes improvements in nonmusical abilities.[122] They argue that such data may show only that smart kids are more likely to take music lessons. They studied 133 undergraduate students recruited from an introductory psychology course, only half of whom were musically trained—and found that the association between music training and intelligence disappeared when the investigators controlled for initial aptitude. The results suggest, they wrote, "that pre-existing individual differences in music aptitude and intelligence predict musical participation. Such participation may then go on to increase music aptitude and intelligence further, but training effects are likely to play a small role in the overall picture." Not surprisingly, the authors' final statement is a variation of the sentence found at the end of many scientific reports: "Future research on musical and nonmusical abilities is bound to find more interesting and nuanced results." The general public may conclude that scientists can never make up their minds; but this is exactly the way science should work, especially in such a complex realm as the brain and human behavior.

A more recent study, a multi-year effort by the Los Angeles Philharmonic Association's "YOLA" (Youth Orchestra of LA based on Venezuela's *el sistema*) and "HOLA" (Heart of Los Angeles program), along with the University of Southern California's Brain and Creativity Institute, attempts rather successfully, in my view, to address this chicken-and-egg conundrum.[123] In 2012, they launched a five-year longitudinal research collaboration to study twenty students, most from disadvantaged areas of the city, at an early age before they began music lessons—in most cases at about the age of six—and tracked their results from the onset of their exposure to systematic, high-intensity music education. They compared the outcomes with a group of nineteen children in a community sports program and twenty-one not involved in any after-school program. So far they have found that:

1) "Music training accelerates brain maturity in areas of the brain responsible for sound processing, language development, speech perception, and reading skills"—all very useful abilities for learning a wide range of subjects of the sort they will encounter in future high school and college curricula;[124] and

2) When the young musicians performed an intellectual task (while undergoing an MRI scan), they demonstrated "greater engagement of a brain network involved in executive function and decision-making"— results supporting the idea that "music training results in a better biologic foundation for everyday decision-making and impulse control."[125]

As we discussed earlier, a different line of inquiry has amply shown that the brains of musicians, studied by newer methods like fMRI, differ from those of non-musicians in specific ways, indicating that music education at a young age, when brain plasticity is greatest, affects the later structure and volume of the brain. And those changes in structure could potentially serve and enhance other abilities, like visual memory and language skills. Musicians have greater ability to pronounce foreign languages, and have superior spatial skills. The fact that, for example, musicians blinded from birth, or at an early age from ocular diseases, can expand their other capacities, including musical ones, by appropriating unused visual hardware in the brain provides a good example of plasticity from another perspective. The Los Angeles studies described above have also shown that children receiving music instruction demonstrated changes in the size of brain regions engaged in processing sound, such as the auditory association areas in the right temporal lobes, as well as in the connectivity between hemispheres in the *corpus callosum*.[126] They concluded that indeed, as we discussed earlier, "music training impacts brain structure," calling upon plasticity to build larger structures and stronger connections.

That potential beneficial effect of early (in life) musical training has become a hot topic lately, just at the time that funding for music education is being withdrawn from many American schools. And that development is particularly unfortunate in view of increasing evidence that

1) musical ability, although requiring some innate physical and mental capability, can be greatly nurtured by disciplined, systematic, thoughtful practice early in life that

2) can build brain structural and functional capacity for music that

3) can probably help in developing a wide range of other skills and capacities throughout life.

Ericsson and colleagues greatly illuminated the age-old question of nature vs. nurture when applied to musical ability, while also establishing general developmental rules. Studies that have extended Ericsson's results are the tip of a growing iceberg of information that supports a critical role for early music education—and better to fill your brain with music at any age than to bash it on the football field. And ironically, the *corpus callosum*, discussed above as being larger among some musicians, may be one of the brain structures most vulnerable to injury inside football helmets that collide at combined velocities of up to thirty miles per hour.[127]

Never did music more sink into and soothe and fill me—never so prove its soul-rousing power, its impossibility of statement.

— Walt Whitman, about hearing the Beethoven Septet while recovering from a stroke

I have found only two types of non-pharmaceutical "therapy" to be vitally important for patients with chronic neurological diseases: music and gardens.

— Oliver Sacks in *Everything in Its Place*, a posthumous collection of his writings

4
CAN MUSIC HEAL?

Byron Janis is a magnificent pianist. I admire his recordings and treasure my old vinyl disk of his Strauss *Burleske*, with Fritz Reiner and the Chicago Symphony. So I was intrigued when I came upon his essay on music, "A Healing Art."[128]

As I read, an image popped into my head of a pot of chicken soup, a remedy still considered therapeutic for just about any ailment. Indeed, sometimes it is—when you need hydration, nutrients, electrolytes, warmth, and loving care from friends and relatives.

Janis's pot contains a variety of good stuff: broad generalizations and assertions like "music enhances the brain's ability to facilitate healing," or "the ancients' drums, rattles and didgeridoos . . . had huge diagnostic and healing properties," and "music is believed to recruit uninjured parts of the brain to compensate for parts that have been injured, and help those parts that are injured recover."

Janis also throws into his pot anecdotes from personal experience. Music "brought back all the joys the house had known," or "slowly brought back her ability to speak." "Many told me how much music had helped their recovery." "Patients went from being catatonic to fully functional." Janis describes a program at Walter Reed National Military Medical Center, where, according to the hospital, "working with actual instruments, patients learn, play, compose and record music."

The program "aims to enhance the healing process . . . enrich the lives of patients, visitors and staff and help relieve the stress often associated with a hospital setting."[129] Novel idea. Good aims. Like in asylums in Bagdad over a thousand years ago:

> In addition to baths, drugs, [and] kind and benevolent treatment given to the mentally ill, music therapy and occupational therapy were also employed. These therapies were highly developed. Special choirs and live music bands were brought daily to entertain the patients by providing singing and musical performances and comic performers as well.[130]

All of the above reflect good intentions. Music can sometimes help some people feel better, at least in the short term. Music can soothe or boost emotions. For many, it provides instant comforting familiarity. Like William Styron in *Darkness Visible*, I find sad music more poignant when I feel sad. Styron was planning suicide until hearing a recording of Brahms' *Alto Rhapsody*. "The music pierced my heart like a dagger," he wrote, "and in a flood of swift recollection I thought of all the joys the house had known. . . . " Franz Schubert memorialized this effect of music in his *An die Musik*, enlisting the words of his friend Franz von Schober:

> *Beloved art, in how many a grey hour,*
> *When life's mad tumult wraps around me,*
> *Have you kindled my heart to warm love,*
> *And borne me to a better world!*
>
> *Often a sigh flowing from your harp,*
> *A sweet, divine chord,*
> *Has unlocked for me a heaven of better times,*
> *Beloved art, I thank you!*

Indeed, among older people, music can trigger memories and bring to mind forgotten words or experiences. And I hope (given the increasing evidence below) that playing my flute every day (and actually practicing thoughtfully) improves my physical and mental health and may help delay Alzheimer's or vascular disasters.

Many medical and most "alternative" therapies are applied for decades or longer. But because it may *take* decades until someone decides to test their effectiveness, many of the untested therapies have enriched therapists more than they have helped patients, at least after hope wears off. Lacking proven, or even tested, therapies, doctors in previous centuries applied leeches, phlebotomy, and tonsillectomy to justify their fees. These therapies are still used, but only in specific circumstances, as targeted treatments—not as universal cures for everything for everyone. Fortunately, music seems unlikely to cause harm, like radiation for acne or spinal fusion for back pain—or injury to other creatures, like the cutting-edge therapy Robert Schumann received for his finger dystonia, which involved "inserting the ailing extremity into the moist belly of a recently slaughtered animal."[131] But we need to learn the specifics of music therapy. Can we target music to treat particular conditions?

Whether and how music might be beneficial or therapeutic is a huge, complex, daunting challenge. What modes of therapy, and in what conditions? What kind of music? Schubert? Bon Jovi? Didgeridoos? More hopes, claims, and programs (and books like this) will undoubtedly arise as scientists begin to seek answers to these questions. Despite the fact that we all think music is good, its therapeutic potential is not self-evident and must be studied and proved in each specific instance.

The discipline of music therapy—"the evidence-based use of music in clinical situations that help people reach desired health outcomes"— often taught in colleges and universities as part of a health sciences curriculum, so it can feed off the burgeoning health care industry—is one attempt to impose some scientific rigor on the situation. Maybe it will help; but too often the term "music therapy" is applied to any efforts, not always evidence-based, to treat medical conditions using music. At least some of those attempts, often well-intentioned, may seem effective if they just provide care, or even just attention, to an afflicted person who would not otherwise receive either.

It also seems clear that in some cases, music can activate a special kind of placebo response: not necessarily one applied to relieve any particular malady, but instead, through a particular response in the brain, bringing about a greater sense of well-being or contentment.

Placebos "are drugs, devices or other treatments that are physically and pharmacologically inert. Placebo interventions do not, by definition, have any direct therapeutic effects on the body. However, all treatments are delivered in a context that includes social and physical cues, verbal suggestions and treatment history. This context is actively interpreted by the brain and can elicit expectations, memories and emotions. . . ."[132] Studies reliably show the success rate of placebos (as measured by self-reports by patients) to average around 30 percent—or higher, if the therapist is caring and convincing, such behavior providing the context.[133] The context of acupuncture, for example, includes ritual, tradition, positive expectations, price—it usually costs more than a haircut—and the perceived competence of a skilled practitioner thoroughly trained in an ancient art proven over centuries. The needles don't even have to puncture, just prick, so long as the patient experiences an effective context. The placebo response is not a product of trickery or deception; it accompanies actual physiological and chemical changes in the reward system of the brain, such as production of endorphins and dopamine, along with changes in blood flow and connectivity, similar to changes evoked by other modalities, like talk therapy and medication and—perhaps?—music. Wounds aren't healed, the causes of illness aren't eliminated, and the outward effects are primarily temporary, but patients come away feeling better—as I do leaving Walt Disney Concert Hall or walking home through the woods after a Gretna Music concert—*and* possibly having experienced some actual salutary changes in brain function and even structure.

Monteverdi wrote his ground-breaking opera *L'Orfeo* in 1607 during a time when, in the words of John Eliot Gardiner,

[T]he emotional life of human beings was becoming a topic of the utmost fascination—with philosophers and playwrights trying to define the role of passions in human destiny, and with painters as varied as Velázquez, Caravaggio and Rembrandt all intent on portraying the inner life of men and women . . . Monteverdi made the decisive creative leap—from a pastoral play, intended to be sung and not spoken throughout, to a musical-drama with emotions generated and intensified by music . . . [134]

Musical treatises of the seventeenth and eighteenth centuries talk about *Affekt*—the character of the music. The performer's role was to evoke a particular *Affekt* or emotional state in his listeners—whether that be joy or contemplation or rage or despair or triumph. The Baroque performer used every possible means to cast his emotional spell on the audience: rhetoric, gesture, harmony.[135]

Intuitively then, music seems to be a promising avenue to explore with regard to the treatment of psychiatric conditions called "affective" disorders. These include depression and bipolar (manic-depressive) disorders. Anecdotal reports like William Styron's suggest that future controlled studies aimed at scientifically confirming this intuition could bear fruit. But the widespread popular impression that music can indeed alter mood, feelings, and emotions introduces a large risk of bias in any such studies. Consider the fact that the generally accepted beneficial effects of both talk therapy (including Freud's methods) and pharmacological antidepressants remain controversial even after more than a century of their abundant use.[136] (One simple answer is that both seem to work in some patients some of the time, but we can't reliably determine when they will work or with which patients, or the extent of the accompanying placebo effect.) The challenges of designing a large-scale, randomized, controlled study of music as therapy are mind-boggling. In a testing paradigm, as just one example, what music should be substituted for a single daily tablet of Zoloft?! The problem is infinitely more complex than testing the effect of an antibiotic in treating an infection.

Affective disorders are often associated with chronic pain—and it is reasonable to expect that music might be helpful in ameliorating pain as well. In fact, music is one of the oldest known treatments for pain.[137] But pain manifests in two very different ways: Acute pain, lasting days or weeks, must be distinguished from chronic pain. A harpist in the recovery room to soothe a patient's short-lasting post-operative pain is a typical treatment for the former. A multitude of research studies of varying reliability have suggested, not surprisingly, that music can soothe temporary pain (if only by shifting attention away from it)—though the effect of the music is very difficult to assess because, by definition, acute pain either resolves spontaneously in weeks or transitions into chronic pain.

And chronic pain is a different and far more difficult problem. In chronic pain, the pain process continues inappropriately *in the brain* long after the triggering stimulus anywhere in the body—a broken leg, a back injury, a surgical incision—has healed. A recent meta-analysis—a synthesis of fourteen randomized controlled trials, selected for their adequacy from a total of 768—"suggest[ed] that music may be beneficial as an adjuvant [one part of a comprehensive therapeutic plan] for chronic pain patients, as it reduces self-reported pain and its common comorbidities."[138] The authors pointed out the important requirement, however, that the music must be selected *by the patient*, from the kinds of music he or she likes. And they added the usual caveat: The fourteen reports remaining after winnowing out the large number of inadequately controlled studies involved a relatively small number of patients, and the results therefore need confirmation.

If music eventually proves to be effective therapy for some conditions, it will be largely as a result of its ability to engage with the plasticity of the brain, as discussed in earlier chapters.

Each hypothesis to be tested must be formulated precisely: Just as you can't cure all ailments with vitamin B-12, you can't just play music or provide drums, rattles, and horns in a physical therapy department and expect improvement! Among dozens or hundreds of variables, experimenters must isolate one, equalize all other variables, study large enough groups to yield valid statistics, and carefully measure accurate indicators of the outcome. And as with all science, one must view results with a healthy amount of skepticism, because it seems likely that many researchers harbor the desire to show that music is beneficial, have an interest of one kind or another in proving that that is so,[139] and are more likely to publish positive than negative results in the growing number of journals hungry to publish any research results. So, for example, imaging methods are still in early stages, and results of these studies need to be confirmed across methods and by repetition. Long reference lists in new open-access, online publications are loaded with studies of varying rigor and validity claiming to prove the benefits of music with respect to all aspects of brain health. But in a time of declining interest in music education vs. the increasing time, money, and interest devoted to sports, such exuberance, in my view, can also be viewed as a healthy development, and this growing evidence shouldn't be dismissed.

Four additional common conditions for which music therapy has shown early promise are aphasia and paralysis after stroke, discussed in this chapter, and Parkinson's and Alzheimer's, discussed in later chapters.

After stroke—a focal destruction of brain tissue as a result of an interrupted blood supply—the nature and intensity of the resulting deficit in functioning depends upon the location of the lesion, usually a "ground zero," variable in size, of totally destroyed brain tissue surrounded by a corona of injured but potentially recoverable tissue. For various reasons, the most common debilitating deficits after strokes are: 1) aphasia—an inability to speak and/or comprehend language, and 2) paralysis. Both occur in varying degrees of severity and often together. Some recovery almost always happens naturally but is often incomplete. The degree of improvement depends upon how much of the injured brain tissue revives and how much of the remaining intact brain tissue—surrounding the stroke or in a similar (homologous) place in the opposite brain hemisphere—can take over the lost functions and make the necessary connections with other parts of the brain. Rehabilitation, the process of trying to maximize that recovery, can be achieved by several methods, most of them physical (e.g., physical and occupational therapy) but not all. Because, as we have learned, music recruits or activates so many different networks in the brain, it makes sense to ask whether, by activating specific parts of the brain during re-habilitation, music might somehow aid in the rehabilitation process.

A "single-blind" study (i.e., investigators evaluating the outcome did not know which patients received treatment) in 2008 set out to de-sign the most intuitive and simple experiment to determine the effects of music on the recovery of stroke patients.[140] The investigators asked, "Does just listening regularly to one's favorite music improve recovery from stroke?" The investigators chose sixty patients who had suffered similar strokes. (Right away, here is one problem: The more each stroke patient is tested, the more diverse abnormalities can be detected.) They randomly assigned the patients to one of three groups: 1) a music group, 2) a language group, and 3) a control group. For two months, the mu-sic and language groups listened daily to their favorite music or their favorite audio books, respectively, while the control group received no listening material. At the conclusion of these therapies, the patients in the music group had recovered more verbal memory and more focused attention than those in the other two groups. They were also less de-pressed and confused. Too good (and too easy) to be true? I would like to see more studies to confirm those results, as would a 2013 Cochrane review (independent review of the scientific methods and results) that concluded that "[t]he results suggest there may be a short-term effect on attentional abilities, but future studies need to assess the persisting effects and measure attentional skills in daily life. . . ."[141]

Because some patients with aphasia have retained their ability to sing, and because brain networks for singing are, in part, the same as those for speaking or may run in parallel with or adjacent to language networks, activating them by means of a technique called Melodic In-tonation Therapy (MIT) has been tried, and has shown promise for im-proving language ability in patients with aphasia.[142] MIT involves 1) the "intonation of words and simple phrases using a melodic contour that follows the prosody of speech" (i.e., putting a simple phrase to a tune), and 2) rhythmic tapping of the left hand with each syllable, in order to increase fluency (to prime the opposite, intact right side of the brain to take over the handling of language, which is usually the task of the injured left side). The hand tapping may couple the sounds to facial articulatory muscles—much as they are coupled when gestures accompany normal speech—and that is probably because of the proximity of hand and speech areas in the cerebral cortex. One study of two patients showed that MIT may have an advantage over standard speech therapy.[143] Many more studies, of course, are needed.

Patients with paralysis (complete weakness) or paresis (partial paralysis) of the hand may regain movement faster if they exercise their fingers on a piano keyboard rather than just tap them on a table (or if finger control is lost, tapping on tuned drums). And that observation forms the basis for Music-Supported Motor Therapy. Having read this far, you might suspect that auditory input in the form of a familiar tune facilitates the movement, just as singing aids speaking in stroke patients, and that is exactly what can happen. There is an increase in neuronal connectivity between sensory-motor and auditory regions, and this was demonstrated by EEG-coherence measurements[144] and the establishment of an auditory-sensory-motor network as shown by fMRI.[145] Other investigators have confirmed these results.[146]

Far more systematic studies are needed, of course, but these provide a beginning. What effectiveness has been shown depends on the stroke having occurred in the cerebral cortex. If, instead, the stroke affected the brainstem, or white matter tracts deep in the cerebrum, in effect cutting the wires from the brain to the muscles, music therapy is less likely to restore movement.

"If I had to live my life again, I would have made a rule to read some poetry and listen to some music at least once every week; for perhaps the parts of my brain now atrophied would thus have been kept active through use. The loss of these tastes is a loss of happiness, and may possibly be injurious to the intellect, and more probably to the moral character, by enfeebling the emotional part of our nature."

— Charles Darwin, in Francis Darwin,
The Life and Letters of Charles Darwin

5
MUSIC VS. ALZHEIMER'S
CAN MUSIC DELAY DEMENTIA?

Alzheimer's Disease, the most common cause of dementia, targets auditory memory as well as other kinds of memory. Alzheimer patients may not remember words or tunes they may have just heard, which is the same as saying they can't learn them. But other tunes, solidified or "hard wired" in memory since childhood, may still be retrievable until the dementia becomes severe. Most of the tunes accompany words that may enable a speechless Alzheimer patient to communicate. Probably these songs are stored in more than one place or in the deeper, more robust, brain networks resistant to the process that causes the neocortex to deteriorate. Those deep musical abilities remain an "enduring fragment" of the person who used to be, or "the residual musical self-system that runs alongside established perspectives on the nature of self." They can be excavated and exploited in therapy.[147]

As discussed in chapter 3, making music can be a major workout for the brain. When begun early in life, playing the piano, singing, and even dancing can stimulate the brain's plasticity, thereby affording it a head start in achieving its greatest potential. Even in adults, playing music—and, probably, attentively and critically listening to music—still stimulates plasticity and growth in the brain. Learning and refining skills, as serious musicians do daily in practice or performance to maintain their "chops," has been shown to preserve gray- and white-matter brain structures during the normal aging process, even in later stages in life.[148] Those later stages are when the brain is generally (not necessarily "normally") expected to undergo loss of substance, in a process called "atrophy."

In retirement, maintaining my musical skills by daily music practice has always seemed to me a far better use of my time than sunbathing on the deck of a cruise ship or watching football on TV. And it's less expensive and more interesting than most cognitive exercises one can do (after purchasing them) on the internet, pursue at a local AARP gathering, or perform in an occupational therapy setting. To cap it off, playing music with others is a good social activity. A recent study of older adult instrumental musicians (active vs. former) supports my intuition: the investigators found that "all musicians (active and former) had higher scores on a test of language (Boston Naming Test) compared with non-musicians. However, active musicians scored higher than both non-musicians and former musicians..." on a test of executive function (see p. 58). They concluded that "there may be continued benefit to participating in musical activities later in life" and that, "in the domain of language, gains from playing an instrument are sustained even if a musician stops playing."[149]

Researchers in 2003 followed older participants to study the relative contribution to maintenance of cognitive abilities of various specific activities—like board games, puzzles, and group discussions— over five years.[150] Those participants who frequently played a musical instrument were less likely to have developed dementia compared with those who didn't. The protective effect of playing music was stronger than that gained from the other activities. Physical activities (walking, swimming, etc.) did not appear to confer any protective benefit with regard to the development of dementia in this particular study. (They have in other studies.)

Other scientists examined the beneficial effects of piano lessons in old age.[151] They compared naive participants—those who had not previously played the piano—randomly allocated to an experimental group (six months of intensive piano lessons) with a control group that did not have lessons. The experimental group received one half-hour lesson each week and was required to practice independently for a minimum of three hours each week. After this period of musical training, the piano players showed improvements on tests of working memory, perceptual speed, and motor skills, while the control group did not.

Investigators at Harvard concluded that

[t]o minimize the deleterious effects of aging on brain function, elderly individuals need to engage in demanding multisensory, cognitive, and motor activities on an intensive basis. Accordingly, a training program that is designed specifically to facilitate brain plasticity, or engage multiple brain regions (especially the frontal and prefrontal areas), may counteract some of the negative consequences underlying disuse associated with aging. One activity that has the potential to stimulate and preserve cognition is music making.[152]

These observations even provide another argument for early music education. It is far easier and more rewarding to take up playing an instrument during adulthood if you have previously done so than it is to start cold, for the first time, after age fifty. A study from the Rush University Medical Center also addressed the question: Can we do anything to slow down late-life cognitive decline?[153] The answer is "yes." "More frequent cognitive activity across the life span has an association with slower late-life cognitive decline. . . ." This benefit was small but statistically significant. An accompanying editorial summarizes and gives more perspective on the main results of the research : "read more books, write more, and do activities that keep your brain busy. . . ."[154]

I would imagine you could extend those results further and argue that frequent and intent listening to scholarly lectures, as they do at Chautauquas around the country (for more information on the Chautauqua Movement, see chapter 18), would have similar beneficial effects. The Rush study also suggests that the more you use your brain at all stages of life, even in childhood, builds more "cognitive reserve" that you can draw upon in later life to compensate for the almost inevitable processes—little strokes, Parkinson's, Alzheimer's, and other chronic neurological diseases of all kinds—that may affect our brains as we age. The experimental methods did not determine whether passive watching of films and videos, educational or not, or, as I like to imagine, seriously listening to (as opposed to just hearing) music would slow cognitive decline. Discussing their results, the authors point out that, in addition:

> Neuroimaging research suggests that cognitive activity can lead to changes in brain structure and function that might enhance cognitive reserve. Thus, occupations (e.g., professional musician, London taxi driver) and leisure activities (e.g., playing Baduk [Go]) that challenge particular cognitive functions are associated with differences in the gray and white matter of brain regions that support the cognitive functions. Importantly, longitudinal studies have documented regional increases in gray matter volume and white matter microstructural integrity over temporal intervals ranging from a few hours to several years in persons engaged in diverse cognitive activities, including studying for a test of medical knowledge, apprenticing as a London taxi driver, reading mirrored words, deciphering Morse code, learning novel color names, and performing cognitive exercises.[155]

After testing middle- to older-age adults, psychologists at the University of Toronto concluded that "[m]usicians outperformed non-musicians on [several transfer tasks and on] a composite measure of cognitive control. The results suggest that sustained music training or involvement is associated with improved . . . cognitive functioning in older adults."[156] ("Transfer" means applying skills learned in one task, like playing the flute, to others—like, say, building a birdhouse—though those weren't the particular tasks tested.) The article, which anyone without specialized training can understand, reviews evidence supporting other benefits of playing music at all ages. It is a good example of what I said earlier about the difference between hopes, aims, claims, programs, and evidence-based science when you talk about good reasons for playing and listening to music.

Another study of 853 subjects controlled for childhood intelligence found that multilingualism may delay the onset of degenerative conditions like Alzheimer's disease. That would make sense in this context, given that music is itself a language, one that can be acquired early in life—and so musicians, at least those who can play from a written score, can be considered in one sense to be bilingual.[157]

Formal and sometimes costly brain-training (cognitive exercise) programs may or may not be evidence-based. One of them, ACTIVE (Advanced Cognitive Training for Independent and Vital Elderly), published results of a study that showed "less decline in self-reported IADL (instrumental activities of daily living). . . Reasoning and speed, but not memory, training resulted in improved targeted cognitive abilities for ten years."[158]

We don't, however, have final answers to any of these questions—just small findings that need to be confirmed in the mosaic of understanding the role of music in the brain, which is only one aspect of brain function. They point to the need for more experiments. A recent sobering consensus report from the National Academy of Sciences that exhaustively reviewed all research investigating ways to prevent cognitive decline concluded that the data for three classes of evidence—brain training, blood pressure management, and exercise—are encouraging but still inconclusive with respect to whether any particular method, medicine, exercise, or cognitive activity can definitely slow or prevent cognitive decline in most aging people.[159]

That is the quality which dance music has—no other: it stirs some barbaric instinct—lulled asleep in our sober lives—you forget centuries of civilization in a second, & yield to that strange passion which sends you madly whirling round the room—oblivious of everything save that you must keep swaying with the music—in & out, round & round—in the eddies & swirls of the violins. It is as though some swift current of water swept you along with it. It is magic music.

— Virginia Woolf, "A Dance at Queen's Gate," from *A Passionate Apprentice: The Early Journals, 1897–1909*

6

Music and Dance
vs. Parkinson's

From the point of view of some physicians and patients, our dysfunctional health care system has brought about little change in the treatment of Parkinson's disease since the first use of L-dopa in 1960. When a patient begins to need medicine for tremor and reduced mobility, she or he begins L-Dopa (usually in the form of Sinemet or its generic equivalent). That, with or without a few adjunctive medications, helps for a few years, may add side effects to the list of symptoms, and then becomes less and less effective as the disease relentlessly progresses. We can't, says the old prevailing wisdom, do much to slow the progression—which, if you live long enough, will eventually bring depression and/or dementia. (So the discussion in the previous chapter applies to this chapter as well.) There can be no better illustration of: 1) the inadequacy of a purely medical approach to help Parkinson's patients; and 2) the truth that any person's (and their family's) experience with Parkinson's depends primarily on what they learn about the condition in order to help themselves.

Almost 80 percent of people with Parkinson's initially consult their doctor for one of four kinds of symptoms, the "motor" symptoms of Parkinson's:

1. Tremor

2. Clumsy, weak limb

3. Stiff, aching limb

4. Gait disturbance

Correct diagnosis may be delayed among patients in the last three categories—especially diagnosis by primary care physicians, who care for half of all patients in the United States with the condition. Say "Parkinson's," and most people and some physicians may not think further than "tremor."

Those of us without a family member or friend with Parkinson's may not be aware of the equally disabling "non-motor" manifestations of Parkinson's, which don't respond well to L-dopa. These manifestations have begun to suggest that the pathology of Parkinson's begins in the medulla, low in the brainstem (according to the increasingly accepted Braak staging model of the disease[160]), from where it spreads upward toward the cerebrum, almost like an infection very slowly creeping up into the brain. On its way up, when the pathology reaches the midbrain, motor symptoms, like tremor, begin. Additional symptoms appear as the pathologic process continues upward in the brainstem and into the cerebrum. The non-motor symptoms that, in varying degrees, add to the distress of most Parkinson patients include:

• Anosmia (loss of sense of smell—and thus also of taste to a large degree—a formerly common, perplexing age-related symptom now known to herald either Parkinson's or Alzheimer's

• Bladder disturbance and constipation

• Dementia

• Depression (often limiting necessary mobility)

• Dysphagia (difficulty swallowing)

• Falls (tripping, fainting, imbalance), a serious, life-threatening complication related to some of the other manifestations listed here

• Heart rhythm and blood pressure increase and/or decrease

• Orthostatic hypotension (lightheadedness, tendency to fall or faint when blood pressure drops on standing up)

• Postural and balance disturbance

• Sleep disturbance, including sleep apnea

- Sweating, increased salivation
- Weight loss (causes uncertain, but an unfavorable prognostic sign)

Even this list (and more comprehensive lists of hundreds of symptoms) may not adequately convey the single often most distressing manifestation in the lives of many people with Parkinson's that has advanced beyond an early stage. That would be "slowing"—of thinking, action, and behavioral responses of all kinds (such as "abulia," lack of will or initiative, a word that dinner guests in Thomas Adés' opera *The Exterminating Angel* sing about while trapped by a mysterious force). Parkinson's patients are also especially distressed by "akinesia," lack or slowing of movement. James Parkinson described people so immobile they appeared to be statues. Hesitation to initiate any movement can literally paralyze. This is a disorder in the domain of time.

Wait a minute! What do we call each section, or each part among several parts, that together make up a symphony, concerto, sonata, or string quartet? A *movement!* That traditional identifying name, a thing, as it were, may lead us to think in stationary terms applied to an object, like a chapter in a book or *objets d'art* that exist in space. But music and dance (and poetry) exist in the domain of time. A movement has a speed or pace; a "tempo" as defined by a "beat"; and a "rhythm" within beats. Each movement proceeds to the next over a period of time, in a sequence carefully planned by the composer.

Music thus has the capacity to entrain: to get your brain on an inner, metaphorical train that clickety-clacks along on rails over and past regularly spaced ties and poles, according to a schedule that keeps the train on time, supervised by a conductor (at least on passenger trains). An orchestra conductor likewise gets his players on the same train: All riders start, travel, and arrive at the same time. A patient with Parkinson's has, in that sense, lost his or her inner conductor, and their brain "train" slows as a result.

Human movement is almost always broken into rhythmic components, performed at a tempo defined by footsteps, arm swings, or synchronous combinations of both. And, not surprisingly, formal and social movement—as in group exercise, marching, or dancing—is very often accompanied by music, so that the beat, tempo, and rhythm can help entrain the movements in synchrony. Music, especially music with a regular beat, has the obvious potential to entrain listeners—including those with Parkinson's who are in special need of that.

The responsibilities of people with Parkinson's and their families are many, ranging from discovering precisely how and when the medicine acts in his or her case in order to find the best dosage levels and intervals, to learning how to mitigate all the symptoms of the disease, medically and in other ways. One of the important other ways is exercise: a non-pharmacological treatment modality that in our time has rightly replaced leeches and bloodletting as a universal remedy for many ills, especially those neurological and cardiovascular in character. (Sitting, of course, may be the least healthy of all human activities.) The effects of exercise are difficult to study and assess for many reasons: It varies in kind, duration, and extent; it is difficult to measure; and outcomes are usually measured by means of self-reporting questionnaires. The latest scientific evidence bearing on the effects of exercise on patients with Parkinson's is either anecdotal (i.e., single-case) or comprises meta-analyses of multiple studies with small sample sizes that have shown a "small but statistically significant" positive effect, accompanied by the usual caveat: More research is needed.[161]

We can wonder whether studies with negative results are ever sent to a publisher. But a growing body of evidence, controlled or anecdotal, overwhelmingly suggests that exercise is good, and actually necessary, for optimal human health. That leaves the decision to or not to exercise dependent on the sentiment "Why bother?" (lazy pessimists) or "It can't hurt and maybe will help" (active optimists). Any kind of exercise—from Tai Chi to tango—is beneficial: It comes down to whatever any individual can do regularly. It is reasonable to assume that the extent of the benefits of exercise directly relates to the intensity and duration of exercise and will probably continue over a lifetime, so long as the exercise continues.

Everyone tends to synchronize with a rhythmic beat, a process called "entrainment," whereby the brain incorporates the external beat, as when dancing, into an internal metronome and uses it to program synchronous movements. Oliver Sacks and others have emphasized that Parkinson's patients with small rapid steps, called *marche a petit pas*, will lengthen and slow their steps when they march to a real march, like "Stars and Stripes Forever," that bandmasters customarily conduct at 120 beats per minute, two each second. Watch David Leventhal of the Mark Morris Dance Company do that in the dance studio.* Videos show how Leventhal and his class synchronize their arms, legs, and torsos to the beat.

Walking, of course, is great exercise, partly because it is available to almost everyone at home without a treadmill, and it can be done in the company of (and in synchrony with) others. Walkers with Parkinson's could play a march on a smartphone and split the music into two pairs of earbuds. Metronomes, especially adaptive metronomes that produce an audible beat that can synchronize with gait, can also be effective.[162]

Alternatively, Parkinson's patients could use a walking stick or staff. Rhythmic placing of the staff ahead along the path creates the beat. When the staff is held loosely, a heavier expanded crown swings forward (like an old wooden metronome), and the tip moves backwards, then forward again, for the walker to take three or four steps past it. The walker can thus coordinate a march in sync with a steady full metronomic cycle.

The neurologist who invented the neurostaff claims, furthermore, that:

*The incorporation of the arms and legs in a whole body motion creates a synergy of proprioceptive sensations providing the brain with additional posture information to deliver better balance and hence psychological confidence.***

Thus, the tip of a staff on the ground or floor provides not only a beat but also a third source of proprioceptive (position sense) signals to the sensorimotor regions of the cerebral cortex that program walk-

* http://danceforparkinsons.org
** http://www.neurostaff.com

ing. Once Parkinson's patients accustom themselves to the walking stick, their small steps may become longer; balance becomes more stable with three points of contact; falls become less frequent; and confidence increases. (I find that to be true for myself when I walk with a neurostaff, and I don't have Parkinson's.)

Of course, you can also use a neurostaff as a baton, to conduct a band playing a Sousa march (which was probably the original purpose of batons now twirled in front of bands). Or to ward off animals or small children.

Exercise is just one way in which people with Parkinson's can help themselves. Singing is another. The film *Alive Inside*[163] shows how Parkinson's patients who can barely speak can sing the same words with gusto when they sing them to familiar tunes known to all, like the "Star-Spangled Banner." Singing in a choir in synchrony with many others is an especially good way to try to preserve the internal metronome that can be stolen by Parkinson's. Singing in a choir is good for lots of other reasons, too.[164] Eminent composer and conductor John Rutter says, "A church or a school without a choir is like a body without a soul." Neuroscientists haven't yet located the soul, but some might say that it lives deep inside the brain, perhaps near the *substantia nigra* (black stripes) in the midbrain—ground zero for many prominent manifestations of Parkinson's.

A new hypothesis is that progression of Parkinson's Disease may relate to the spread of an abnormal accumulation and "misfolding" of a normal protein called alpha-synuclein. Not being efficiently cleared from cells, it forms a kind of "uncollected garbage" within cells (like amyloid in Alzheimer's), and is the actual content of the "Lewy bodies" that pathologists have seen for more than a century under microscopes in the *substantia nigra* in the midbrain of Parkinson's patients, and that are critical for making the diagnosis by microscopy. Alpha-synuclein can also be found in the nasal cavity and gut of victims of Parkinson's, suggesting that there may be a prodromal (very early) phase of the condition during which a mysterious agent—whatever it is (or they are) that causes Parkinson's—probably enters the body through the nose or the mouth.[165] It, or its evil effect, travels to the brain through the olfactory or the vagus nerves—the former from the nose, the latter from the gut. Along its path to the brain, this agent causes progressive alpha-synuclein clumping as well as various types of havoc including non-motor symptoms, as it makes its way up the brainstem. When it and the alpha-synuclein reach the *substantia nigra*, more prominent clinical signs of Parkinson's begin.

There is a possibility, therefore, that Parkinson's Disease is caused by some undetermined toxic agent(s) from the environment that could be in anything we breathe or put into our mouth.[158] Investigators testing a (literal) thousand possible agents found two that promoted the spread of alpha-synuclein, including a common beta-blocker used to treat high blood pressure, along with two other common medications that slowed the spread of the disease and may prove to be new effective treatments.[166]

I rolled a quire of paper into a kind of cylinder . . .
— René Laennec

7
THE FLUTE
AND THE STETHOSCOPE

After a lifetime as a physician and flutist, I only recently became aware of the same duality in the career of the young French doctor René Laennec, inventor of the stethoscope.

In 1816, I was consulted by a young woman labouring under general symptoms of diseased heart, and in whose case percussion and the application of the hand were of little avail on account of the great degree of fatness.[167]

Such "percussion and the application of the hand," augmented by placing the ear directly on the chest, were used by Laennec's contemporaries to examine the heart. We might wonder whether the fact that Laennec played the flute might account for the novel way he solved his problem.

I rolled a quire of paper into a kind of cylinder and applied one end of it to the region of the heart and the other to my ear, and was not a little surprised and pleased, to find that I could thereby perceive the action of the heart in a manner much more clear and distinct than I had ever been able to do by the immediate application of the ear.

Laennec named his instrument a "stethoscope" (from the Greek *stethos*, chest or heart, and *skopos*, observer). He eventually constructed other instruments out of various materials, and called the technique "mediate auscultation."

> *The most dense bodies do not, as might have been expected*
> *from analogy, furnish the best materials for these instruments.*
> *. . . Bodies of a moderate density, such as paper, the lighter*
> *kinds of wood, or Indian cane, are those which I always found*
> *preferable to others. A greater diameter renders its exact appli-*
> *cation to certain parts of the chest, impracticable; greater length*
> *renders its retention in exact apposition more difficult, and*
> *when shorter, it . . . frequently obliges [the doctor] to assume an*
> *inconvenient posture.*

Flutes in Laennec's time were almost all made of wood. Dense wood, such as maple or cocobolo, was preferred, and the bore of the flute was larger in diameter than the bore of Laennec's original stethoscope, a difference that still obtains. One might wonder whether Laennec as a flutist was especially sensitive to differences in the sound of blood flowing through the heart, as he presumably was to the air flowing across the mouthpiece of his flute—the only wind instrument that turns air directly into sound without a solid vibrating reed or a pair of lips.

Flutes today are made of wood, silver-coated brass or nickel, silver (sterling, coin, or French), gold, and platinum—the last being the most dense of all the precious metals. The diameter of the section with the blow hole is less than the far end section (foot) so that it has a "conical bore," as do all modern flutes today. William. S. Haynes of Boston, who made my flutes, said that in 1905 he made one silver flute for every hundred wooden flutes, but by the 1930s, influenced by an influx to America of French styles and players (in particular, Georges Barriere and Marcel Moyse), he began making mostly silver flutes—eventually, in reverse, a hundred of them for every wooden flute. The wooden flute has shown indications of a comeback recently after the short tenure in Boston of

Jacques Zoon, a fine player on a wooden instrument.

Every flutist has a preference, though most today play on silver French models with open holes in the keys and thin light walls, valued

Figure 2. This art was not made from my piccolo by Max Hunsicker, one of Gretna's many artists and artisans, but it perfectly captures my life-long distaste for playing that infernal instrument.

for their ability to project a brilliant sound from within a large orchestra into a large hall. The science supporting preferences for different materials is shaky because of so many variables: the size, shape, and depth of the embouchure hole, the thickness of the wall of the tube, and the configuration of the conical head joint, in addition to each player's own unique embouchure. It took more than half a lifetime for me to realize that I should have shopped more extensively for the instrument best suited for me.

While the modern flute, like most woodwinds, has evolved into a costly work of art made of valuable precious metal, like a coveted piece of jewelry, the evolution of the stethoscope has produced a simple flexible plastic tube available in drugstores for under forty dollars. Casually thrown around the neck, the stethoscope has become the iconic emblem of authority for a physician or nurse, especially in TV advertisements. More importantly, it is also a routine way for some physicians to connect with a patient, to "lay on hands." Some physicians, like the authors of the article cited at the beginning of this chapter, lament the displacement of the stethoscope by modern techniques like ultrasound, where the "mediate" part of the auscultation is a technician with a machine.[168]

If I should ever die, God forbid, let this be my epitaph:
THE ONLY PROOF HE NEEDED
FOR THE EXISTENCE OF GOD
WAS MUSIC
— Kurt Vonnegut, *in A Man Without a Country*

8

Usher Me Out with Music

I recently read Dr. Susan Mitchell's article "Advanced Dementia" from a New England Journal of Medicine issue of a few years ago: lots of authoritative information from many patients about this inevitably progressive, memory-robbing, ultimately life-ending condition, mostly manifesting as Alzheimer's Disease but also with Parkinson's Disease and in other less common forms.[169] Though the incidence of advanced dementia is decreasing (at this point in time) in this country, probably because of improving health care and lifestyles, the disease now afflicts five million persons in the U.S., a number that is expected to more than double by 2050 because of an expanding older population,[170] and possibly also because of increasing toxins in the polluted air we breathe and substances that we are exposed to by other routes. We can't predict when dementia will end a life: That depends on when and which complications arise, most commonly in the form of eating problems and infections, especially pneumonia.

> Medications are costly and relatively ineffective. Treatment decisions for patients with advanced dementia should be guided by the goals of care; providers and patients' health care proxies must share in the decision making. After the provider has explained

the clinical issue to the health care proxy, framed in the context of advanced dementia, the proxy should then articulate the goal or level of care that aligns with the patient's preferences, such as treatments that promote comfort only, all medical interventions that may prolong life (e.g., mechanical ventilation), or something in between (e.g., administration of antimicrobial agents) that may help the patient return to pre-acute-illness baseline status. In prospective studies, more than 90% of proxies stated that the goal of care was comfort.[171]

If I should ever suffer the misfortune of this condition or any form of extended pre-morbid decline, my goal of care will indeed be comfort only, even before my dementia becomes advanced. We have talked about the healing power of music, but maybe we should also consider its comforting power. Though music can't heal a wound or restore failed kidney function, it can temporarily restore an Alzheimer patient's ability to speak (by singing) or help access her memories (like a "can opener," according to music therapist Gretta Sculthorpe). What's more, music has no side effects as do tranquilizers, which calm at the expense of blunting further any remaining trace of self and sensibility, causing life-threatening falls, or worse.

In *Musicophilia*, Oliver Sacks remarks, "music therapy in people with dementia . . . seeks to address the emotions, cognitive powers, thoughts, and memories, the surviving 'self' of the patient. . . . It aims to enrich and enlarge existence. . . ."[172]

Sacks appears in the film *Alive Inside* showing music in action, enlivening dementia patients.[173]

Based on weak evidence (two cases) that musical taste deteriorates as dementia progresses, I'll probably suspect my own dementia if my taste changes from classical to pop music.[174] But I doubt I'll ever be totally comforted by "Somewhere Over the Rainbow," or by my high school "fight song." Rather, both would undoubtedly irritate me! But evidence tells us that the music that best unlocks the "surviving self" in patients with dementia is the music that means the most to each individual—

which usually was hard-wired deep in the brain during a person's second decade. In any given case, experimenting may be necessary in order to select the appropriate music.

Here are a few suggestions for my own health care proxy.

Just before the New Year, I purchased a DVD of Claudio Abbado conducting the Lucerne Festival Orchestra in Mahler's *Ninth Symphony*. The Ninth was Mahler's farewell to the world: "Each passing minute takes us closer to the grave. Death is awful in its inevitability. We will rage and fight against it, but in the end, something bigger than we can imagine will force us into acquiescence." (The German music critic and journalist Shirley Apthorp wrote that in the liner notes.) The Ninth gave rise to the despondent *Late Night Thoughts While Listening to Mahler's Ninth Symphony* by Lewis Thomas,* who contemplated late in his life the possibility of nuclear Armageddon (which seems to have recently crept back into my consciousness; maybe my dementia will remove it).

Mahler's own end was premature, in 1911 at age fifty-one, caused by subacute bacterial endocarditis, a condition from which he could have been saved fifty years later by antibiotics and, if also needed, cardiac surgery. Maybe writing the Ninth gave Mahler some comfort. Abbado was about seventy-six years old when he conducted the recording I speak of, five years before his more timely, but no less regrettable, end.

The Abbado performance on the DVD is, according to Apthorp and in contrast to, say, the popular Leonard Bernstein recording, "fluid" rather than "angular," "driven" rather than "accepting," and "talkative" where Bernstein was "silent." However you try to describe it in mere words, the amazing performance kept our entire party on New Year's Day totally rapt after dinner. No one asked me to check football scores! We all respected the "Abbado Silence" after the last quiet note died away. Speechless, we wiped away tears.

Everything about the DVD is exquisite: the musicians, hand-picked from the best orchestras in Europe; the filming that, I hesitate to say with

*An old recording of the Ninth preserved the last performance of the Vienna Philharmonic before Hitler killed many of its musicians and put the orchestra out of business when he made Vienna part of the Third Reich in 1939. [175]

Lucerne on my bucket list, offers many advantages, such as close-ups of the players and conductor, over what any member of the large audience in the hall, Kofi Annan and Simon Rattle (the conductor) included, was able to experience. The sound would have been better on a good system or lush and full with headphones. The view from all angles of Abbado conducting without a score a work he has known all his life, was memorable. Orchestra members, entirely immersed in the music, effortlessly moved and swayed with him. A lot of art has probably been inspired by the idea of the Resurrection. None comes closer, in my view, to matching the profundity of that idea than the recording in this set of Mahler's *Resurrection Symphony*.

Armageddon à la Lewis Thomas is not part of the business model of Amazon. As if they were watching us on New Year's Day, they delivered a few days later an offer to my inbox: Mahler's Symphonies, Nos. 1 through 7, recorded at the Lucerne Festival by Abbado and his orchestra! I snapped up a "like-new" package of four DVDs from one of the "other vendors," for forty-three dollars plus shipping! I only discovered several weeks after it arrived that the producers had slipped in a bonus Prokofiev *Third Piano Concerto* by Yuja Wang along with Mahler's "Five Rückert Songs" sung by the sublime Magdalena Kožená, mentioned only in small print on the album cover. If my time was near, my proxy would have been overjoyed.

Maybe when my time comes, Amazon's algorithms will know that I would also like to listen to a recent exquisite recent Chandos recording of Rachmaninoff's *All-Night Vigil* by the Phoenix and Kansas City Chorales.

How often would I like to have you here with me, for your B is leading a very unhappy life and is at variance with Nature and his Creator. Many times already I have cursed Him for exposing His creatures to the slightest hazard, so that the most beautiful blossom is thereby often crushed and destroyed. Let me tell you that my most prized possession, my hearing, has greatly deteriorated. . . . I must withdraw from everything. . . . Needless to say, I am resolved to overcome this, but how is it going to be done?

— Beethoven, July 1, 1802, in a letter to Karl Amenda[176]

9
TREASURE YOUR HEARING
YOU WILL NEVER REGAIN WHAT YOU LOSE

Our sound engineer at Gretna Music will tell you that I have complained since Adam and Eve that our jazz concerts are too loud.

I point out to him that a harpsichord or a classical guitar can be heard well from any of the 720 seats in our playhouse. But the next night, sounds of an electric guitar may pass through two ten-foot banks of speakers (destroying directionality, as the sound comes from the nearest speaker, not from the guitar), through a soundboard as large as a grand piano and then across the surrounding farms almost to the state capital in Harrisburg. Often, performers turn up their stage monitors (speakers pointed at them that allow each player to hear himself among the amplified sounds of the others)—so high that their sound alone fills the hall. And (as I usually try to ignore) we, as do much of the world's population, already live in clouds of air[177] and noise pollution.[178]

Globally, hearing loss is the fourth leading cause of disability.[179] In the United States, the prevalence of hearing loss doubles with every ten-year increase in age. Approximately half of Americans in their seventh decade (sixty to sixty-nine years of age)[180] and 80 percent who are eighty-five years of age or older have hearing loss that is severe enough to affect daily communication. Professional musicians may be over-represented among these groups.

Imagine my reaction on a nearby porch after one of Gretna's loudest concerts when a neighbor appeared in this t-shirt:

Figure 3: This t-shirt was actually sold by a pop music festival that shares the Gretna Playhouse with Gretna Music.

I have lost hearing over a lifetime of playing and attending concerts, not to mention living in the "clouds" of other unavoidable anthropogenic (human-made) noises. I have "presbycusis," a word that implies (falsely) that hearing loss that comes with aging is normal, or inevitable at some particular age.* Typically for someone my age, I have lost my high-frequency sensitivity (for sounds above 2,000 Hz, or vibrations per second), so in some situations, like in noisy restaurants, I have trouble understanding speech—say, distinguishing a sibilant "s" from an "f" from a "t"—unless I watch the speakers' lips. Fortunately, I

---

*An exception to the rule is that after teenage years we all "normally" lose some ultra-high-frequency perception—that is, with respect to sounds in the range of 17 kHz. That fact impels, and enables, the production of gadgets like the "Mosquito" to deter teenage loitering around stores at the mall by blasting a sound at 17.4 kHz. Ultrasonic pest deterrents utilize the same principle.

don't have any trouble hearing music (as long as it's not painfully loud).

Two main reasons account for most progressive age-related hearing loss: 1) the DNA in your inherited genome, and 2) the cumulative effect of a lifetime of exposure to sound. The former you can't avoid; the latter you can. Sound waves (vibrating air), after being collected and focused by the pinna (the outer, visible part of the ear), enter the ear canal and cause the eardrum to vibrate. The vibration is transmitted by a chain of three ossicles (tiny bones) to the cochlea, a small, delicate organ embedded (for protection) in the thick temporal bone. The ossicle at the end of the chain, the stapes (which looks like a horseshoe), acts like a drumhead on the bell-like opening of the cochlea. Sound travels through the tapering bore of the cochlea, as if backward through a French horn, all the way to the narrow or mouthpiece end of the coil, stimulating the microscopic hair cells that line the bore as it passes by, much as wind flows over a field of grass.

If you were a hair cell living near the opening of the cochlea, it would be like sitting under a drumhead, and these hair cells—those closest to the drumhead—are the ones that resonate with higher-frequency sounds and thus seem to be the most vulnerable to damage. Loud sounds cause hair cells to disappear—as putting mileage on your car thins the tread on your tires—very slowly and imperceptibly. You can replace a tire, but you can't replace hair cells, and they don't regenerate (with some exciting new possible exceptions[181]). So the number of hair cells you possess at any time in your life is the most you will ever have. You can destroy hair cells with loud sounds during any time of your life, but you may not notice hearing loss until enough of them are gone. And by then it is usually too late, because you have a permanent hearing impairment.

Warning: If your hearing loss is only in one ear, you may have an acoustic neuroma (a.k.a "vestibular Schwannoma"), a slowly-growing benign tumor inside the skull but outside the brain, that starts growing at the far end of the acoustic nerve in its canal through the temporal bone. It usually grows so slowly that the hearing loss it causes may not be noticed until to late to be reversed. The tip-off to its presence is that it almost always is one-sided. Another less-sensitive tip-off is that it can appear in people of all ages, not just older people. An MRI with injected material (that contains the chemical element, gadolinium) to increase contrast is the only way to diagnose an acoustic neuroma. Surgical removal is the only effective treatment. It is such a sneaky character that I know more than one malpractice lawyer who specializes in cases in whom it detection has been delayed!

Loud sounds can also cause tinnitus (the medical name for ringing in the ears), but probably by a different mechanism that probably involves nerve cells and circuits in the cochlear nucleus in the brainstem or the auditory cortex of the temporal lobe, an example of dysfunctional plasticity, as discussed in chapter 11. Tinnitus and hearing loss, which have a common cause, often occur together. Hope for reducing tinnitus depends on gaining the ability to temporarily rejuvenate cortical plasticity, allowing cortical organization to return to normal.[182] Early in life we may be cavalier about exposure to anything, including loud rock music—especially if it is essential to our emerging identity. Musicians are increasingly aware of the problem. The next time you see an orchestra, watch the woodwind players, who sit in front of the trumpets and trombones. Sound-blocking baffles behind their chairs are relatively ineffective—as are other measures, like separating players on a large stage, or on risers—so you may see them inserting earplugs when the brass players in the back row play especially exuberantly, aiming at the backs of the bassoon players' heads.[183] The European Union, in fact, mandates earplugs in orchestras and other loud workplaces.

The orchestra pit may be the most hazardous of all environments for musicians, trapping players amidst sounds from all directions (not to mention clouds of rosin dust from dozens of string bows). An orchestra is a sound-hazardous environment, with sustained sound levels regularly exceeding 85 decibels (dB) (the recommended maximum to ensure safety), over as many as thirty hours a week of rehearsals and concerts. Such sustained and long-term exposure probably makes classical musicians even more vulnerable to hearing loss than jazz or rock musicians, many of whom may not have to practice or rehearse for such long periods, at least not over a lifetime.

But it was a surprise to me to learn that, for a musician, the greatest hazard to hearing comes from one's own instrument, both while playing in the orchestra and during additional hours of individual practice![184] We know this because researchers put little microphones on both ears of instrumentalists: Players of asymmetric instruments like the flute or violin (sending slightly louder sounds more to one ear of the player) experienced asymmetric exposure to levels of sound as high as 98 dB, exceeding the safe maximum in individual practice as well as in ensembles of all sizes. On stages and in pits, we can assume that the sound of one's own instrument compounds with the sounds of surrounding instruments, especially violins and brass, to regularly exceed levels considered safe with respect to avoiding hearing loss.

There is some evidence that sustained sounds (meaning sounds lasting between two and thirty minutes, depending on loudness) are more damaging than sound that is periodically interrupted. But it certainly makes sense to avoid loud sounds altogether, if only by carrying a pair of earplugs in your pocket (or on a string around your neck)—or better yet, wearing sound-blocking earphones, noise-canceling or not.

♫

The cause of Beethoven's deafness has long been debated. In the days before modern brass instruments and electronically amplified sound, "sound-induced" deafness might have been less likely. A copy of a postmortem examination, written in Latin and rediscovered in 1970, reliably shows his deafness to have been an acquired rather than inherited condition. Surprisingly detailed, the exam reflected a modern "clinico-pathologic conference" (CPC) approach to Beethoven's lifelong health, his hearing loss, and, most distressingly, his final illnesses:[185] From now on, I'll have to consciously repress feeling the agony he suffered during his final weeks wherever I listen to his music. Beethoven continued to compose in between episodes of vomiting, jaundice, and punctures that removed gallons of fluid from his abdomen (now called paracentesis to remove ascites). After a thorough study of the detailed clinical history of Beethoven's two final weeks and the autopsy report, the participants in the modern CPC agreed that a single condition could not explain all of Beethoven's lifelong medical problems, which culminated in his death at the age of fifty-six. The single disease that best explains most of his manifestations, including his deafness, is syphilis. In the nineteenth century, syphilis was called the "great imitator" because, over the course of decades, it could eventually affect almost all the organ systems in the body, causing, among other conditions, eye disease, liver disease, and skin disease—and it accounted for at least 7 percent of cases of unexplained sensorineural hearing loss in that era.[186] In Beethoven's case, the abnormalities—mostly infections—discovered in the temporal bones were so extensive that he probably had both conductive (in the ear canal, eardrum, and bony ossicles) and sensorineural (in the cochlea and auditory nerve) hearing loss. (The autopsy description of Beethoven's brain—"The convolutions of the brain were full of water and remarkably white; they appeared very much deeper, wider, and more numerous than ordinary"—do not encourage reliable speculation as to whether syphilis had affected brain function in his case.)

Paradoxically, we know most about Beethoven, the man, during the last twelve years of his life, his musically most fruitful years, when he was totally deaf—because he was forced to communicate in writing. His "conversation books," like Leonardo's notebooks, provide extensive details about his daily life, thoughts, and contacts.

♫

New evidence shows that musicians, accustomed to listening critically, maintain better than others the ability to understand speakers when surrounded by ambient noise in crowded, noisy situations like parties.[187] In such circumstances, lip-reading can also help. But other evidence indicates that late-life hearing loss (and visual loss, too) promotes accelerated cognitive decline and earlier onset of cognitive impairment in older adults, a finding consistent with lots of prior research demonstrating a significant association between greater hearing loss and poorer cognitive functioning on both verbal and cognitive tests.[188] Many different mechanisms may be at play in this relationship, including, for example, the social isolation that hearing impairment may cause and depression related to an inability to hear, as well as impairment of the process of trying to understand garbled verbal information. After reading about plasticity in earlier chapters, one might imagine that a reverse form of plasticity might accompany impaired verbal input into the auditory cortex: Instead of building new circuits to handle new information, the plasticity reverses under the influence of less demand, as existing unused circuits begin to disappear and atrophy (loss of brain substance) ensues. Or perhaps other regions of the brain start to be enlisted in attempts to improve understanding of verbal input—visual regions, for example, perhaps involved with lip-reading—distracting them from other critical tasks and thus impairing attention.

It might also be worth pondering why the higher-frequency hearing loss that impairs my understanding of speech does not diminish my hearing, or enjoyment of, or sensitivity to, music. As best as I can determine, music sounds to me the same now, as a septuagenarian, as it did in my youth. My ability to perceive pitch (via my almost-absolute pitch), intonation (slight differences in pitches), timbre (differences in the quality of sounds, like those between a flute and an oboe), tempo, dynamic range (between loud and soft), and just about all other musical qualities I can think of remains unimpaired. Put simply, I believe the answer is that my brain, after years of listening to music with normal hearing, has developed expectations, or templates, and automatically corrects the sounds that I *do* hear to those that I *should* hear, without any effort or awareness from me. That theory, alas, does not apply to some of my friends with a more advanced hearing impairment who can no longer enjoy certain music—especially singers or instruments with higher-pitched voices or sounds. A corollary worth investigating is the possibility that replacing speech with song might well slow the process of decline, of both hearing and cognitive ability. Instead of struggling for an hour to understand some of what a speaker is saying, attending a concert might not only be more enjoyable but also therapeutic!

Before your next Metallica concert, just remember the first sentence in a recent issue of *Consumer Reports*: "Our shoppers purchased . . . forty-eight hearing aids . . . ranging from $1,800 to $6,800 per pair." And hearing aids don't replace normal hearing and come with their own set of problems, especially for people who enjoy music.

Just intonation [or temperament], with its pure fifths and pure thirds, may be an ideal, charged [Vincenzo] Galilei, but in practice it is a fantasy. Singers continually adjust as they go along, automatically altering the intervals they produce to create beautiful sounds. In any case, the fact is, the human ear easily learns to accept tempered intervals. Indeed, it has been clearly shown on instruments that equal temperament works wonderfully.

— Galileo's father, Vincenzo (c.1520), quoted by Stuart Isacoff in *Temperament: How Music Became a Battleground for the Great Minds of Western Civilization*

10
WHAT'S YOUR TEMPERAMENT?

Temperament in music, a fascinating topic discussed in two excellent books,[189] relates to the arithmetic of how the "interval" or space on a keyboard between the first and eighth tones of an octave is divided into twelve smaller intervals to generate the notes in the major and minor scales of Western music, called "diatonic" scales. This division is based upon a principle of ancient mathematics determined by Pythagoras in ancient Greece, which states that the vibrating frequency of the highest note of any octave is exactly twice that of the lowest note (usually measured in Hertz [Hz], or vibrations per second).

Intervals have names. Playing a C scale up from middle C on a piano, the first white key you reach is D. The interval between C and D is a second: It is a whole step up from C. Then you come to E, the third note of this scale and an interval of a third from the C, equal to two whole steps. Next come the fourth, fifth, etc., notes—defining their respective intervals measured from middle C—until you reach the eighth note. The interval between that eighth-note C and middle C constitutes an octave.

The "key" of a scale is named according to the note you start on: C, A, F, etc. All diatonic major scales have whole steps and half steps ("semitones") in a specific sequence: whole, whole, half, whole, whole, whole, half—thereby sounding like the common scale that our brains (using its plasticity to make templates, as I discussed in chapter 2) have come to know and love since childhood: *do re, me, fa, so, la, ti, do*. Each major scale—that is, each scale in the major "mode"—has those same seven intervals separating seven different notes; but in order to have diatonic scales that start on each of those seven notes, there must be five additional notes within each octave to make the half steps: the sharps and flats identified on the piano as the black keys. If you play all twelve notes in any octave from bottom to top—ascending the scale totally in semitones (that is, half steps) by pressing every black and white key as you ascend—you get a chromatic scale.

In total, there are twelve different notes (and therefore eleven corresponding intervals) within the interval of an octave, all separated by half steps—so composers can write music in any of twelve different major keys. Ditto with respect to the minor keys (that is, scales in the minor "mode"), which have different sequences of notes and intervals. That makes twenty-four keys in all. Hence Bach's *Well-Tempered Clavier*: two books of twelve preludes and twelve fugues each, one prelude and one fugue in each book composed in each of the twelve major and twelve minor keys.

Now imagine blowing the lowest note (the "fundamental" note) on a bugle (with no keys) or on any wind instrument with all holes closed. Then tighten your lips and blow a little harder. Out comes a note an octave higher, with twice the frequency. It's impossible to get any other note in that first octave! Blowing a little harder and tighter produces a note 3/2 higher in frequency than the fundamental (representing an octave plus a fifth), then 4/2 (twice the frequency, i.e., two octaves) higher than that, then 4/3 (two octaves and a third) higher, and 5/4 (two octaves and a fifth). Those are the only notes a bugle can play. (That's why you see dozens of valveless brass instruments on walls of quaint restaurants in Europe; each can play only those notes, in different keys.) What you have just produced is called the "harmonic series," a succession of notes related to each other by simple fractions: the respective frequency relationships of an octave, a fifth, a fourth, and a third are 2:1, 3:2, 4:3, and 5:4. All stringed instruments employ the principle of Pythagoras that stopping strings at simple fractional lengths can create any note of a scale. If you divide a string on a violin into those same simple fractions, you get the same intervals (octave, third, fifth, etc.) Any other fraction, say 4/3.875 (the denominator is my mortgage rate) gives you a sour note, nowhere near any note on any scale.

These simple intervals have also been called "pure," "just," "divine," or "natural," because they seem grounded in physical laws of nature. This simple fractional relationship fascinated Pythagoras and early scientists and philosophers so much that it led them to wonder whether studying such a natural, divine relationship—what some have called "the music of the spheres"—could unlock fundamental laws of the universe. Maybe that's why the study of music, not just playing it, was considered an art, along with mathematics, geometry, and astronomy, in the *quadrivium* of the medieval university, which, along with the *trivium*—grammar, logic, and rhetoric—made up the original liberal arts.

But we have a problem. If you start at the lower end of a keyboard and tune a succession (called a circle) of twelve perfect fifths (C–G, G–D, D–A . . .), you eventually arrive back at another C, but it is an imperfect C (not exactly twelve times higher than the starting C: That C (stacked on top of twelve perfectly tuned fifths) is higher (by a ratio of 1/1.014; a difference called the "comma of Pythagoras") than the perfect C on top of seven perfectly tuned octaves. (Not so divine!) So, to fit (that is, to tune) twelve intervals into an octave, you have to somehow shrink all or some of the intervals: You must "temper" them, and so they (or some of them) become no longer simple fractions. There are innumerable ways to balance this budget, so to speak, depending on which intervals you choose to contract. Each way is called a "temperament" and there are dozens of them, if not hundreds. This challenge attracted some of the greatest minds of earlier centuries—Pythagoras, Plato, da Vinci, Galileo, Kepler, Descartes, Newton, Rameau, Rousseau—and caused plenty of controversy and conflict (and probably a few deaths), because it was considered a philosophical problem as well as a musical one. (I can only wonder how our current Congress might tackle it.)

In Western music, the problem has been approached in the fashion of a bricklayer. He must fit twelve bricks into a metaphorical "octave wall" slightly too short to fit all twelve but too long for eleven. Most bricklayers would simply shorten one or some of the bricks, or the mortar. (Well, maybe. I'm not a bricklayer.) Alas, you can't do that to just one note of one scale and expect to maintain the possibility of harmony in any chord in which that note is used. And because our brains have come to expect intervals of notes are considered natural or divine, you can't just substitute notes of random frequencies. (Though modern composers such as Georg Friedrich Haas have; he hears in the octave interval — or indeed, the entire range of human hearing — a spectrum of any number of pitches that he can compose with instead of notes on a scale.)

To solve the musical (though maybe not the philosophical) part of the problem, hundreds of solutions, called "temperaments" (or patterns of fitting in the bricks), have been proposed over many centuries. Any particular temperament can seem to affect the character or feeling (happy, bright, sad, dark, etc.) of a piece of music, at least to listeners able to sense very small differences in pitch. In certain temperaments, music played in certain keys can sound good or bad to different listeners. Some temperaments simply cannot be used for playing in certain keys because they require discordant (sometimes called "wolf") intervals to balance the sweet harmonious ones. Composers choose keys for their works based on which key seems most appropriate in a particular temperament: The key of D major might sound happy and bright in Valotti I but sad and dreary in Valotti III temperaments (at least to the educated ears of serious musicians of each era in music history).

A Dutch mathematician, philosopher, physicist, and engineer named Simon Stevin (1548–1620), sometimes called Stevenus, proposed one of the earliest solutions to the temperament dilemma. Inspired in 1580 by the writings of Vincenzo, the Italian lutenist father of Galileo Galilei, he fit the twelve intervals into an octave by calculating an interval separating all semitones by the twelfth root of two ($^{12}\sqrt{2}$) (an algebraic number that extends *ad infinitum* to billions of decimal digits, if you have the time and inclination). In this so-called "equal temperament"

(ET), to build a scale from the fundamental tone you multiply the frequency of each successive note by twelfth root of two (or approximately 106 percent).

♫

So why have you not paid much attention to musical temperaments until now, even if you listen to and love lots of music? I knew about them because I dabbled in harpsichord building when I should have been working in my medical lab as a young Assistant Professor. Before the computer age, I had an electronic tuner that could be set to a range of different temperaments by inserting different slotted cards.

With skill, you can change the temperament of about five octaves of strings of a harpsichord almost as fast as on a violin or guitar, or at least in minutes. But tuning a piano that has three strings for most of its eighty-eight keys) takes far longer and is not practical during a concert. For that reason, during the nineteenth-century ascent of the piano, some uniformity had to be imposed—especially because composers increasingly wandered into a wider range of keys. In any given temperament, the first sonata on the program might have sounded good, but maybe the second, in a different key, did not. A piano had to be able to handle, without tuning, all keys which a composer might use: say, B Major, with five sharps. Therefore, the universal "equal temperament" (ET), the compromise by which almost all notes in the octave were slightly but equally altered, gained favor. By 1890, James Lecky in "A Dictionary of Music and Musicians," had anticipated what I'm getting at.[190] By 1917, this change had been so accepted and established that almost no one today hears or pays much attention to temperament, excepting some in the HIP (historically informed performance) community. One of them, in despair it seems, went so far as to ponder whether ET "ruined harmony."[191] (What it certainly did was put an entire field of temperament specialists and scholars, except for a few holdouts, out of business.) The controversy may continue.

One result of ET is that probably only those with perfect pitch can appreciate that any particular key has a unique character. The rest of us can't sense a difference beyond that between major (mostly happy) and minor (mostly sad) keys (though that is a gross oversimplification). (If composers or listeners have synesthesia—and most of those who do also have perfect pitch—and then different keys might be "heard" in different colors.

I've alluded elsewhere to Mozart's ability to accurately identify any note regardless of its source. He had "absolute" or "perfect" pitch (AP), an ability to accurately identify any note, which we now know is a product of: a) the requisite innate brain connectivity at birth, supplemented by b) training (to be able to accurately link a pitch to a key name) during a particular period early in life when the developing brain is most receptive to such training—that is, during a "critical" period for the development of AP. Because he definitely had AP, we can assume that Mozart also had a very sensitive ear for detecting very small differences in pitches, such as the differences that separate notes tuned slightly differently in one temperament from how they are in another.

And Mozart could hear an oboe tuning note A and reliably say if it was 1 Hz (or less) too low or too high than the pitch of the A customary in his musical community at the time. A at that time, however, would have had variable frequency, depending on a musician's geographical location (as high as 465 Hz in seventeenth-century Venice; as low as 392 Hz in eighteenth-century France), but it perhaps would have been close to 415 Hz, a common pitch for his day that we now call the "low pitch" in early music of previous centuries.[192] But Mozart had learned that ability from reading and hearing many notes early in his lifetime. A contemporary Mozart with AP would answer A on hearing a note played today at 440 Hz, a worldwide standard (though still variable to a lesser degree: It was 446 in Boston in the 1960s, possibly because electronic tuners had not yet become universal, as they are today).

There is nothing about A-415 (in Mozart's time) or A-440 (today) that is grounded in the natural or physical world, in or outside of the brain (such as the laws of gravity, the Pythagorean relationship of the sides of a triangle, or the earth's rotation). That standard tuning frequency of 440 Hz has emerged to be in roughly the middle of the frequency spectrum for music—taking into account, of course, the frequency spectrum of human hearing, which ranges from about 20 to 20,000 Hz, or that of human singing, which extends from 80 to 1,500 Hz. The extension of the hearing spectrum into the upper hearing range allows us to distinguish a wide range of note quality (also called timbre), because the quality or character of a note depends on harmonics or, and described by James Lecky, as "a whole series of soft ancillary tones—sonic shadows that ring above every *do* or *re* or *mi* like unbidden harmonic ghosts."[193]

♫

What explains the fact that we listen quite happily to Bach and Handel's music at a higher pitch than they did when they wrote it? Believe it or not, it's neural plasticity. Over the lifetime of everyone reading this, the traditional A 440 pitch that we all have heard from birth—and thus *learned* unconsciously—has been the contemporary standard pitch in all genres of music. That is roughly 25 Hz higher than it averaged in the eighteenth century, and a difference that most non-musicians could detect if notes were played in rapid succession, but possibly not if they heard them separated by hours or days. While most musicians could distinguish notes even under the latter condition, neural plasticity can enable most of us to accept a change in pitch in hours, if not minutes.

So you can see where I'm going here. Consider a parallel example of visual plasticity: Each time an optometrist prescribes for me a new pair of glasses, I may experience a little discomfort when I wear them for the first time. That may include the illusion that square or rectangular images (windows, doors, a TV picture) don't appear to have right angles, or a straight line may appear curved or a vertical one slanted—maybe accompanied by a little nausea (from vertigo). The optometrist cautions that it may take some time "to get used to them"; and indeed, those distortions reliably return to normal after a few days or even a few hours, because of neuroplasticity—which allows me to adjust to the new glasses as what I see aligns with information entering the brain from other senses and with my brain's existing templates, formed from long experience, that confirm that a wheel is round, a window is a perfect rectangle, etc. Furthermore, after wearing the new glasses for months or even years, if I replace them with my *old* glasses, I don't experience those unpleasant distortions or sensations in reverse, at least not to the same degree. It seems as if my brain must have retained an old template that had formed when I initially adjusted to that *old* pair of glasses. There seems, in other words, to be some permanence to each adjustment.

A more extreme illustration of plasticity in the visual system was afforded by experiments in the 1950s and 60s in which prisms built into glasses shifted visual images in either a vertical or horizontal direction— say, ten degrees to the left or, in some cases, completely upside down. Within minutes, subjects began to compensate: Images that had initially appeared shifted by the prisms gradually returned to their original position—that is to say, to where they actually were. Subjects began to experience less difficulty walking, or picking up objects that had appeared displaced to ten degrees away from where they actually were; and within days to weeks they were virtually totally adjusted, at least to the smaller displacements. We can speculate that the brain had first increased the amount of neurotransmitters enabling the connections needed for a new template, and then built more permanent and stable anatomical ones. That was adult brain plasticity in action; childhood brain plasticity is far greater, that is, faster and greater in extent.

A similar accommodation process, I am told, happens after the fitting of new hearing aids. And most patients remark after cataracts are removed that the world appears to be much brighter—but only for a short time, until the brain's plasticity readjusts. (Of course, increased clarity of vision and *some* of the increased brightness remain, because the partial opacity caused by the cataract is gone from the path of light to the retina.)

I would argue, therefore, that the experience of hearing any particular temperament, especially during the early, "sensitive" period, before age eighteen, conditions one, we might say, to that temperament. It seems plausible to speculate that plasticity builds connectivity templates for probably most of the temperaments that we have listened to with any regularity. In adulthood the same process may take place, though most likely at a slower pace and requiring more exposure to a new temperament. Of course, if there is some investment, whether occasioned by pride, reputation, or a political or financial interest, in any particular temperament—as may have been the case in the past—that might slow or prevent changes otherwise enabled by plasticity.

In the seventeenth and eighteenth centuries, before motorized travel and recordings and when both musicians and listeners were more isolated, their templates, we can speculate, tended to be more parochial or location-dependent. If, for example, a twenty-six-year-old German like Handel traveled to Italy with German templates in his brain, he theoretically, at least, may have been surprised at first to hear not only different—and, to him, strange—Italian pitches but also different Italian temperaments. At the relatively young age of twenty-six, and perhaps without any investment in his German temperament, he probably could have adjusted fairly quickly to the new pitches. The world is a different place now, however: The piano is ascendant over the harpsichord, and all listeners and musicians have templates for the equal-tempered scale. And all the music they hear, live and recorded—at least that composed in the Western tradition—is in the same ET temperament.

We don't know, yet: 1) how templates (or whatever we decide to call the results of learning enabled by plasticity) change over time, or 2) how pitch perception—sensitivity to small differences—changes with aging over time. (I would guess that individual variations are great and depend on many factors.) When I listen to old recordings of Pablo Casals, I have a reaction similar to that of a cellist quoted by David Blum and cited by Ross Duffin.[194] The cellist was, "a performer not without talent but who had early in life accommodated to equal temperament. Hearing Casals for the first time, she exclaimed, 'It is *soooooo* beautiful—but why does he play out of tune?'" Casals used expressive intonation, a technique not as systematic or calculated as settling on any particular temperament, which varied pitches according to the place of notes in a phrase. By this technique, for example, leading notes in a phrase—perhaps leading to a cadence, or a climax—were played at a slightly higher pitch, so as to move the phrase along or anticipate the point toward which the notes were leading (or perhaps not, if they were heading toward a surprise, such as a deceptive cadence). By the time of the recording she heard, Casals was, shall we say, of a certain age and spent long periods playing alone—or, some would say, in a horizontal way, playing only one line of music (usually Bach)—as opposed to having to adjust his pitch in a vertical way to match others playing with him. (The way such adjustments are made by a string quartet, I would venture to suggest, are one of several factors that give each ensemble it distinctive sound.) And the longer Casals played in his expressive intonation form of temperament, the more the strength of his templates for that style increased, and the more his intonation seemed normal to him. That, too, is plasticity!

In human behavior, temperament is generally considered an innate configuration of inclinations or predispositions determined by brain connectivity at birth, some of which are immutably hardwired and most of which are resistant to change and constrained by limits. Temperament in music, by contrast, according to my argument, is a taste or preference, a product of experience and social context or custom: software, if you will, most susceptible to programming changes during sensitive periods in early development, but also, to a lesser degree, able to change in adulthood. Character might have actually been a better term for musical temperament, because it develops through the interaction of predispositions and environment.

Has equal temperament established itself forever as the standard tuning? Depends on whom you ask.

"When I have to play for anyone, I'm overcome by an anxious inhibition of my fantasies that drives me to despair . . . the third finger seems really incorrigible."

—Robert Schumann, diary entry, 7 May 1832

"[A] kind of paralytic condition, manifested first in that [the fingers] *possessed only a weak feeling, and second in that so far as movement was concerned, they no longer responded willingly."*

— Moritz Emil Reuter, M.D., Schumann's physician, in a medical affidavit, Peter Ostwald in *Schumann: The Inner Voices of a Musical Genius*

11

MUSICIANS WITH DYSTONIA
WHEN PRACTICE MAKES IMPERFECT

The music of Robert Schumann remains vital and wondrous in the universe of classical music—and perhaps we should thank dysfunctional brain plasticity for it. At the age of twenty-two, when he was studying law (against his wishes) while also a piano student competing with his teacher's daughter Clara, with whom he was in love against her father's vehement wishes—even as he was drinking too much, actively searching for his sexual identity, feeling anxious and depressed, and fighting loneliness after his teacher took Clara away for months—Schumann began to lose control of the middle finger of his right hand. He tried various remedies to no avail, including mechanical contraptions as well as a cutting-edge medical treatment of 1831: "inserting the ailing extremity into the moist belly of a slaughtered animal."[195] Thereafter, Schumann turned from performing to writing music and writing about music.

Though it lies at the intersection of two major domains, modern medicine and musical pedagogy, dystonia in musicians seems to have been largely appropriated by the medical domain, especially since the recent surge of interest in the medical problems of performing artists. When Schumann, in his day, sought medical help, he instead found a quack remedy. Quack remedies still exist today—as do misguided ones, such as surgical cutting of ligaments and tendons. Modern neuroscience could offer

Schumann a better understanding of his problem, thanks to accumulating observations of cases and neuroimaging; but modern medicine could probably still not restore Schumann's full ability as a pianist. Botox injections, in addition to various drugs and behavioral therapies, may help some dystonia victims to some extent—but often at the expense of side effects incompatible with playing an instrument.

One obstacle to successful treatment is that we face many diverse individual instances of the condition. Typically, the disorder occurs in varying degrees and locations and reflects different kinds and combinations of symptoms. And though we can easily divide cases into two broad categories: extremity dystonia (in the arms and fingers) and embouchure dystonia (affecting the lips, tongue, and teeth), each musician suffers from his or her own version of the condition, and no single solution fits all cases, in the way insulin improves diabetes. But we have achieved a better understanding of the basic nature of all of the manifestations of the condition: They originate in parts of the brain. Unfortunately, there they are subject to myriad influences, including genetic heritage, personality, lifestyle, toxins not limited to alcohol, sleep patterns, emotions, life stress, and performance anxiety.

Even some of the conventional statistics, like those relating to the prevalence of the condition, are uncertain, because they derive from self-selection of subjects, self-evaluation ("on a scale from 1 to 10"), and data collected retrospectively, via interviews and questionnaires. The diagnosis in many of these cases may not be certain. Swallow this conclusion from an expert in the field:

> *Taken together, epidemiological findings indicate that the amount of workload of the respective body part, the complexity of movements and the degree of spatial and temporal sensorimotor precision as well as the level of social constraints associated with the musical performance were related to musician's dystonia.*[196]

So our understanding is still limited, even as we try to help.

♫

Dystonia in musicians may be a dead-end branch of the evolutionary tree: a maladaptation that happens when the human brain (of certain vulnerable humans; as I discuss below) is called upon time after time to do one of the most complex motor tasks of all, beyond the limits of capability of most of us—like playing a Schumann (not to mention a Scriabin or Rachmaninoff) etude.

> *After all, we suggest that manual dexterity has reached the end of adaptation and exaptation—at least in the conventional style of music making. The advent of disorders such as musicians' cramp may well be a warning sign of biological limitations in individuals. . . who are especially susceptible to disturbances in neural plasticity.*[197]

Dys- (bad) *tonia* (muscle tone) means involuntary muscle contraction: the inability to *not* contract muscles when that would be appropriate, as when controlling each finger independently or shaping an embouchure on the mouthpiece of a woodwind or brass instrument. The resulting loss of control is not due to weakness. When a flexor muscle contracts, its opposite, an extensor muscle, must relax: If both the biceps and triceps contract at the same time, for example, the forearm doesn't move or performs a clumsy writhing movement as both muscles try to prevail. The long recognized generalized familial form of the condition, *dystonia musculorum deformans*, affects most muscles usually early in life. The focal form, often task-specific, usually involves small integrated groups of muscles used repetitively for years to perform the same particular task. Dystonia in musicians is task-specific.

A common form of task-specific focal dystonia, writer's cramp, illustrates a key characteristic of task-specific dystonia: It usually appears only when writing with a pen or pencil—not, for example, when typing or using a knife or fork. A violinist may experience dystonia, usually in the left hand, when playing the violin but not when playing the larger viola (which, admittedly, most violinists don't do very often). My teacher had it when he reached his sixties: He became unable to control his third and fourth fingers independently, but only when playing the piccolo, smaller than the flute. So it is clear that sensory input—signals sent to the brain from muscles and joints as they contract and move— plays a role. The problem involves sensory-motor integration.[198]

In a minority of cases, dystonia may spread from one task to another—from playing the guitar to typing, for example—indicating that some individuals may indeed have a greater genetic vulnerability than others.

Writers can sometimes minimize cramping by using a fat pen— which feels different in the hand than a thin one and sends slightly different signals back to the brain. Such a maneuver is called a "sensory trick." A similar ruse may be employed by victims of torticollis, involuntary head turning. If they gently touch the side of the chin on the side the head turns to, using no effort to overcome the rogue rotator muscles, the torticollis may stop—temporarily. Musicians can learn sensory tricks too.

♬

Well-known musicians with dystonia include pianists Leon Fleischer and Gary Graffman and violinist (of the Tokyo Quartet) turned conductor Peter Oundjian. They and other victims, like Schumann, turned their careers around in mid-life and made other distinguished musical contributions. But musicians with lesser degrees of the problem, those unaware that they have it, and those who have chosen not to "out" themselves for fear of losing engagements may compromise the statistics relative to its prevalence, which is now thought to extend to at least 1 percent of all classical musicians. Some musicians who believe they have dystonia may actually have one of a variety of other neurological problems that mimic dystonia; that's why a neurologist with special competence is necessary.

Embouchure dystonia,[199] more recently recognized, is more difficult to overcome; few of its victims can continue their careers. (Some have, as I describe below.) Uncertainty also attends the reason for the observation that, in most series of collected cases, men are far more often affected than women, by a 6-to-1 ratio.

Instrumentalists most affected by any type of dystonia seem to be pianists, guitarists, violinists, flutists, clarinetists, and trombonists, roughly in order of the perceived complexity of execution. (Like many of the numbers above, these data come from the German musical community.[200])

Classical musicians are those mostly affected, not only because they practice Ericsson's ten thousand hours so as to compete for limited opportunities, but also probably because they are subject to more strict restraints than are jazz and pop musicians. You can't, for example, play a difficult Chopin etude in an easier key, rewrite an Elliott Carter quintet to make it playable up to tempo, or make repeated failed articulations in the trumpet opening of Mahler's *Fifth Symphony* part of your signature jazz style. You have to "nail" the notes exactly as written, exactly at the right time, and without the advantage of three strikes.

♬

Ironically, in the past, the cause of musician's dystonia was thought to be overuse—that is, overuse of the machinery of making music: muscles, tendons, joints. But now we know that to the extent that the term "overuse" applies, it more aptly refers to overuse of a part of the brain. Musicians who play casually, or who play technically simple music, are rarely affected, because they don't have to practice for many hours. In one sense (and only one sense), the problem seems to me comparable to wheels making ruts in a road by using the same path over and over: Eventually, the ruts become too deep, and your vehicle can only follow the ruts, even if they go to the wrong place.

I really don't intend to contribute the term "brain ruts" to the discussion, but I will try to simplify a little pathophysiology. So: Impaired sensory-motor integration underlies dystonia.[201] Sensory-motor integration is critical for the "muscle memory" that musicians speak of: One parcel of the cerebral cortex sends command signals to the fingers or embouchure, which, in responding, send signals back to another parcel. Both the initial motor message and the sensory reply are integrated and routed to other parcels, some of which record that activity. Those recordings—making up a growing library of muscle memory—help facilitate, or prompt, the same activity each time it occurs again, first by enhancing neuron-to-neuron-chemical transmission in the activated connections, and eventually by building more anatomical connections to help perform that particular task. The former may explain why you improve by multiple repetitions of a passage during one practice session; the latter, enhanced anatomical connections, probably explain why the passages you learn today stay with you longer—much longer, if you're in your sensitive adolescent learning period. Ultimately, innumerable repetitions build a network of lasting connections to enable fingering, for example, from an F to F-sharp. Of course, the numbers of cells and connecting elements involved number in the millions.

One indicator of brain plasticity is the enlargement of a specific area of cerebral cortex (gray matter on the brain surface) in response to the relevant intensity and duration when that area is called upon for use. For example, the areas of motor and sensory cortex in the right hemisphere of the brain activated by fingering a violin with the left hand expand with practice to a larger size than the corresponding areas in the left hemisphere, because the fingers of the bowing right hand, while not unimportant, perform less complex individual tasks than do those of the left hand.

Areas, and thus actual volume, of brain cortex expand (we see this via MRI) as they develop more fibers (axons), connections (dendritic spines, synapses), brain cells, and support matrix. Motor and sensory cortical areas for fingers and lips lie adjacent to one another in the frontal and parietal lobes. They overlap to some degree—and theoretically, at least, expansion of the network for one finger, say the third, could invade the network of another, say the fourth, and vice versa. I wonder whether the facial movements of violinists and pianists—obvious when they are filmed close up (see any video of Leon Fleisher playing, or conducting*)—reflect this proximity of fingers and face in the cortex: activity in the finger area spilling over into the face and lip area. Obviously, this hypothesis would predict that the likelihood of embouchure dystonia is increased in musicians with finger dystonia, and vice versa; some data suggest this may be true. But exactly what happens on a microscopic or cellular level to cause dystonia remains uncertain.

Studies have shown that at least some musicians with dystonia have a genetic vulnerability for it: Their brain's neural firmware may have been abnormal from birth. And evidence suggests that their individual finger areas in the cortex are indistinct or overlapping, at least more so than in the rest of us. Most of them, of course, would never have noticed that defect if they hadn't stressed their brains by long, hard practice, though some—more than among the general population—might have experienced other forms of dystonia—such as writer's cramp, torticollis, or blepharospasm (eye closing)—or noticed them among family members and/or ancestors. Exactly what this inherited firmware defect is, and what genes are involved, has not yet been determined, but more evidence can be expected from thorough explorations of family histories, as well as techniques like fMRI and electrical recording of brain activity.

Finally, any human symptom—headaches, dizziness, blackouts, back pain (a neurologist's daily bread)—can be caused or magnified by depression and anxiety (often unrecognized by the victim) and relate variably to stress. Musician's dystonia is no exception: Enduring a divorce, a succession of failed auditions, or performance anxiety can exacerbate the condition. There are good reasons to incriminate the increasingly rigorous orchestral audition as a causative factor. Perfection is the goal when you compete with hundreds of other candidates for one chair, but there are inevitable casualties in the process, as evidenced by so many principal players felled by dystonia.

♫

When it comes to dystonia in musicians, "treatment" doesn't seem to be quite the right word, at least in the sense of medical treatment. Neu-

* Watch Leon Fleisher tell his story on PBS: https://www.youtube.com/watch?v=FZLvhZvO2v4.

roscience has provided a better understanding of musician's dystonia, but so far, treatments based on this knowledge—Botox, medications, behavioral therapy—have only raised hopes, and succeeded partially in a few isolated cases. And prescribed rest periods have rarely helped, in my personal experience.

That said, an important first step is to consult a physician—in almost all cases, a neurologist—who has special competence and experience in evaluating musicians. (If a consultant does not request you to bring your instrument to the consultation, he or she doesn't have either.) Such consultants are rare, because the problem is rare and few neurologists have seen any patients who have it. This first step is important, because a host of other neurological problems can be mistaken for dystonia, like ulnar neuropathy, early Parkinson's, etc.

If the diagnosis is indeed dystonia, the neurologist will assess the possibility that the one potentially effective purely medical treatment might be helpful, and to what degree (which is rarely 100 percent) it might help. That treatment is an injection into carefully targeted small

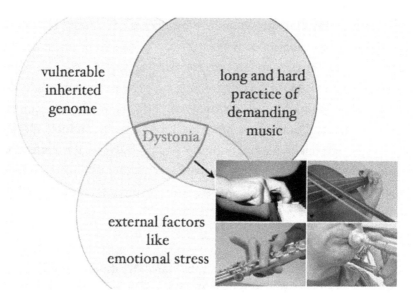

Fig. 4, Causes of dystonia in musicians (Photos from Hans-Christian Jabusch and Eckart Altenmüller, "Focal Dystonia in Musicians: From Phenomenology to Therapy," Advances in Cognitive Psychology 2, 2–3 (2006): 207–20)

muscles to weaken those that inappropriately contract when they shouldn't. Choosing the correct one or more small muscles is a very difficult task.[202]

For now, I believe that good problem-solving music teachers may also offer promising strategies. Most are based on the principle of re-learning (in computer jargon, reprogramming, rebooting, or restarting) from scratch in the realm of the particular problem, be it bowing, fingering (with some wind players), embouchure shaping, or some other. This slow, starting-over change in practice behavior might, as with aphasic stroke patients regaining the ability to speak, generate alternative networks and pathways in the brain—a detour around the ruts in the road, if you will.

This method was used successfully by trombonist David Vining, who described his struggle with embouchure dystonia in Chamber Music magazine.[203] He restarted his trombone career by practicing musical passages while just blowing into the instrument without buzzing his lips (and making the sound that the instrument amplifies). Only months after playing "air trombone" did he begin to relearn how to produce a sound as if he were a child learning it for the first time. Any wind player could try the same strategy.

That strategy falls into the realm of the sensory tricks mentioned above. Similarly, flutists have had occasional success by applying tape to the plate around the hole they blow across to make the sound, by changing to an instrument with a different feel, or installing a variety of handles on their instrument so that holding it sends different signals to the brain. String players can try instruments of different sizes, and perhaps of different balance. (I am not aware of any attempts to play left-handed, or of pianists switching to the harpsichord or organ.)

One might ask whether musicians who learn bad playing habits from the start may be more vulnerable to dystonia later—but I am not aware of evidence addressing that question. That information would be difficult to obtain in any case, and what one teacher considers bad habits may be tolerable or normal habits for others.* (Think of Glenn Gould whose seating and hand positions, if adopted by students, would horrify some teachers.) Nevertheless, Vining believes that his initial intense approach to playing (one that I have observed in other trombonists), which involved employing more effort than necessary to create an embouchure, may have contributed to his problem. When he restarted after studying the Alexander Technique and similar ones, his new approach was more laid-back and relaxed.

You might also ask how one might minimize the risk of contracting dystonia in the first place. The answer is, we don't know, but that won't stop me from speculating. I would say to young musicians: Relax, stay laid-back, don't push it; practice slowly and deliberately and stop before you become frustrated over any particular passage. You can always try it again tomorrow. Substitute regular daily practicing—one or more sessions—for long, intense sessions in which you try to completely master a difficult passage all at one time. In the beginning, all musicians learn to play fast passages slowly, gradually building up to the desired tempo. Take any passage that elicits dystonia and slow it down to a speed that avoids the problem, and then play that repetitively—every day. Do the same with others like it that employ the same fingers, and that you can play over and over without experiencing dystonia. Wear new ruts into the road.

If something like dystonia appears after a period of playing, or if intense practicing seems to make a passage worse, stop playing and start again an hour or more later, or tomorrow. Avoid anger and frustration. Take a break! If you tend to be tense when playing, by all means, investigate a relaxation method like the Alexander Technique.

We are at a similar point in understanding sleep disorders. We don't have a universal, single—let alone simple—treatment that works for everyone. But we do know enough about the problem to begin to develop recommendations for good sleep behavior, under the heading "sleep hygiene." So what I'm recommending here is perhaps what we might call "practice hygiene." In both cases, and especially in the case of dystonia, we are talking about a method that takes months if not longer to show

---

* Of course, some bad habits can lead to other problems down the road, like pain, fatigue, and tendonitis.

results—perhaps as long as it took to master your technique when you were in junior high school— and an effort that never ends.

Personally, I have learned that dystonia can be more of a problem when one is insecure with respect to a given passage of music because of inadequate practice or rehearsal—so that another aspect of rehabilitation can be to learn potentially troublesome passages cold, starting slowly, even to the point of learning them by memory. Greater confidence minimizes the chances of any problem developing, including dystonia. Often when working on difficult passages, I have to stop myself and think, "Relax, lay back, the planet will not stop rotating if you don't immediately get this right!" Of course, a variety of relaxation techniques, along with good sleep habits and exercise—indeed, all healthy lifestyle activities in general—can help to reduce stress and improve the chance of success in any endeavor. All easy enough to say but not necessarily to accomplish—especially with an audition or performance approaching— and by no means a cure for every problem.

Though I have until now favored pedagogical methods to treat dystonia, I don't entirely dismiss the possibility of medical ones in the future. As discussed in chapter 9 regarding potential treatments for tinnitus (another form of dysfunctional plasticity), successful treatment depends on temporarily rejuvenating cerebral cortical plasticity so that the aberrant cortical cells and circuits—the cortical map, if you will—can be rectified, possibly through magnetic stimulation, medicine, or other means. Early attempts to do so have met with success, at least with rats.[204]

Readers with dystonia may have tried some of the above strategies that might apply to them. Because I suspect that we hear more about career-changing failures and too little from those who have succeeded in managing their disorder, especially to the point of being able to resume playing, their testimony could be helpful. Since I have learned about this problem, I believe I have been able to detect early signs of potential dystonia in myself and apply some of the techniques above, thereby avoiding worsening them.

Understanding the basic science underlying dystonia could be the first step in overcoming it, by means of altering and adapting practice techniques. This is not a condition where doctor shopping—or, "You're the doctor, treat me"—often succeeds. Once a competent neurologist has confirmed the diagnosis, one alternative might be: Ask a good music teacher—one experienced in solving problems. And teachers too should take heed, especially the demanding, slave-driver types. (I can only wonder what contribution Schumann's old teacher, Fred Wieck, made to his distress.) Or talk to colleagues who have overcome the problem and consider adapting their methods to your problem. Gamma-knife thalamotomy may prove to be a safe and possibly effective option for some cases.[205] More study may allow us to predict which cases will benefit from this technique before a gamma knife burns a tiny hole into the thalamus, one of the bodies of gray matter deep in the brain. For now, however, the prognosis remains uncertain, and careers continue to be altered.

Nearly all levels of education today neglect exposing the rich history of the West to young people, and that's tragic; they have been deprived of their own cultural inheritance. "Most people know almost no music conceived before their own generation and are indifferent to tapping into the artistic triumphs of past ages" [Jacobs said], a vast reservoir stretching back centuries.

—Sharon Kilarski, "Organiast Paul Jacobs: The Classics Give Purpose to Humanity's Suffering" (*Epoch Times*, Sept 22, 2016)

Living composers are still getting some performances these days, but they almost never hear their pieces again.

—Eric William Lin, "Pulsecheck: Is Orchestral Music Still a Living Art Form in 2017? Extrapolating Trends from 175 Seasons at the New York Philharmonic" (November 2017)

Being the true voice of one's time is . . . roughly forty thousand times as vital and important as being the assumed voice of history. To be the expressive medium of one's own age is . . . a far worthier aim than historical verisimilitude. What is verisimilitude, after all, but perceived correctness? And correctness is the paltriest of virtues. It is something to demand of students, not artists.

—Richard Taruskin, *The Modern Sound of Early Music*

12

WHAT'S THE MATTER
WITH CLASSICAL MUSIC?

Reconciling these three views remains a challenge, especially in our world today. Looking over the "white, rich and almost dead" grayheads in classical music audiences, anxious observers have long predicted the demise of classical music along with that of its listeners. More recent data from the National Endowment for the Arts confirms that the current classical music audience is indeed older and (like funding for classical music) has continued to diminish over the past few decades. Although the music's death hasn't yet occurred, such predictions have intensified, and terminal illness may never have seemed more imminent than it does now.

Orchestras and dance and opera companies have gone bankrupt. Corporate, foundation, and government support and individual patronage and ticket purchases have plummeted. When Jane Alexander, chair of the NEA, resigned in 1997, she accused Congress of trying "to drive a stake into the heart of Federal funding for the arts."[206] Classical-music radio is making a heroic last stand in a few major markets. The media disregard concerts and lay off classical music critics; large media companies have turned to other music, as the lifespan of the CD seems to be nearing its end. Schools have dropped music education. It was frightening to hear someone say the other day, "We don't know whether anyone will be listening to Beethoven fifty years from now," or read frustrated critics wondering, "What will the mp3 generation listen to next?"

During a recent period of more than average orchestral distress in Philadelphia, critic Peter Dobrin characterized one root of the problem as undercapitalization—which, he noted, prevents the orchestra from expanding and improving activities necessary to generate more revenue, a vicious cycle. I can only try to imagine the bewilderment of Bruno Walter or George Szell reading Dobrin's recommendation, which is to determine "[w]hat is the job of this orchestra, in this city, in this day and age?"[207] It's difficult to reconcile these realities with the "great notion" that Pere Portabella's 2006 film *Die Stille Vor Bach* inspired in another critic: "[M]odern Europe was built on a foundation of classical music, which, as a result, endures tenaciously there."[208] Though even there it is perhaps enduring less tenaciously now.

Speculation about the reasons for these developments has intensified as well. The fast pace of modern life. The growth and evolution of electronics that brings all kinds of entertainment into the home, making concert attendance seem unnecessary—let alone that tickets are expensive, and traveling "downtown" and finding parking are inconvenient.

There is also the assumption that enjoyment of classical music requires education and refined taste that, like a taste for fine food or wine, requires years of education, not to mention considerable wealth. Classical concerts may intimidate and deter the uninitiated, who don't know all the conventions and etiquette—the rules and regulations, as it were—like when to clap and when not to. We classical music devotees have been accused of snobbery—of believing that only classical music is real music: of worshipping the permanent collection and ignoring the music of our time. Younger generations may reject what they imagine as snooty formal affairs with somber, old, arrogant white male musicians in archaic evening dress.

"Classical," of course, also connotes a sense of history—another concept that often seems to be disappearing, or at least diminishing in value. The term "classical music" became widely used by 1830,[209] even then to indicate music written by "deceased great composers" and performed by great artists, though many of those great composers were actually not deceased, and in fact were still performing their own music. In the 1970s, Richard Taruskin, sole author of the monumental *Oxford History of Western Music*, wrote:

> [I]n the absence of a vital creative impulse classical music has become a chill museum. (The vitality, alas, is with other forms of music, in which performers behave very differently.) Our classical performers are the curators of their heritage, not its proprietors. They are sworn to preserve it and trained to be uncreative. So if you are creative, you have to hide the fact. You have to come on (to yourself as well as others) as a better curator, not a revamper.[210]

The contemporary jazz pianist Vijay Iyer would probably agree.[211] After years of learning the "correct" way to play the music of long-dead composers by means of formal lessons on the violin, he decided to find his own creative voice on the piano—without a teacher. And in the course of that process, he created his own music.

♫

Attention span has been defined, in a survey of Canadian media consumption conducted by Microsoft, as the amount of concentrated time [expended] on a task without becoming distracted, and it can be measured, under proper conditions.[212] The Microsoft report in 2015 (not peer reviewed, hardly qualifying as science, to be sure) concluded that the average attention span among Canadian subjects had fallen to eight seconds, down from twelve in the year 2000. Imagine an orchestral player with an attention span that short! Listening to classical music obviously requires less attention than playing it—it's natural for your mind to wander during a symphony—but the music does proceed from a beginning to an end—in a narrative, so to speak. That progression, sonata-allegro form being only one, and a simple, example,* is a distinguishing characteristic mainly of classical music. Like a novel or poem, it takes you on a musical journey and inspires your own visual and mental images. At a concert, as at a play or film, you don't expect to be distracted by hot dog and beer vendors. The current generation (iGen?), with a habit of texting or checking e-mail every eight seconds, is unlikely to be able to withstand Schubert's heavenly length. Unfamiliar with the sustained attention required by the nineteenth-century concert tradition, they are accustomed to the freedom afforded by pops concerts or sports events to walk around, cheer, and get a beer, listening with what both the Hebrew and Christian bibles, and others, call "careless ease."**

Speaking of sports fans, we should perhaps consider the notion of "fandom," a phenomenon that has always puzzled me but that may apply to music as well as sports. A recent discussion offers the best explanation I have read:

> [F}andom [is] a means of telling [oneself] who [you] are. Sports fandom has become, to borrow a term from the philosopher Michel Foucault, a practice of subjectivization—a phenomenon in which individuals subject themselves to a set of behavioral regulations, and by doing so, acquire a sense of their own identities. Just as a practicing Christian may create and obtain new forms of self-knowledge through confession, prayer and the observance of Lent, a sports fan can come to understand himself as a particular sort of person—a Southerner, for example, or a "real man"—by adhering to certain rituals, like reading the sports page and watching ESPN every day to gather more and more knowledge about his team, by talking with other fans about that team in the right ways (and proving that he knows more than them), by learning and participating in the songs,

* The Sonata form (also *sonata-allegro form* or *first movement form*) is a musical structure consisting of three main sections: an exposition, a development, and a recapitulation. It has been used widely since the middle of the eighteenth century (the early Classical period).
** "For the turning away of the simple will kill them, and the careless ease of fools will destroy them." Proverbs 1:32

chants, dress, tailgate rituals, game-day traditions and home décor choices of its fans.

The extraordinary reach of football into fans' lives makes perfect sense when we see it for what it is: the most popular mechanism in contemporary America for cultivating a sense of self that is rooted in a community. In a world of uncertainty, fragmentation and isolation, sports fandom offers us clear winners and losers, connection to family and community—and at its best, the assurance that we are really No. 1. [213]

Long before football, in Europe—at least in upper socioeconomic levels—music had fans. During the height of the recording era in America, there were fans of the "Big Five" orchestras or their godlike conductors, like Toscanini and Leonard Bernstein in New York; and classical music fans had their own publications, like *Musical America*. Concerts, conductors, and orchestras from all around the country received entire pages of space in the front sections of major newspapers.* Opera, with its superstars, opulent productions, and cultish attraction, may still retain the largest classical-music fan base in the United States, not necessarily amounting to a majority of classical-music lovers. The Los Angeles Philharmonic has fostered fandom for the charismatic Gustavo Dudamel, but it doesn't come close to that for the Lakers. I identify myself as a fan of music, classical and some other, but most of my contemporaries have turned to sports. I don't see many empty seats in the stands at sports events, based on what I see as I pass by ESPN going through cable channels (and on one required physical presence at a Virginia Tech football game last year, with more than 60,000 in attendance). I don't imagine there are empty seats in stadiums for a Rihanna tour, either.

Putting all these thoughts aside, I would argue that classical music and classical music concerts are potentially still very healthy and relevant—and not only because increasing numbers of children all over the world manage to discover that they want to play it, according to the late

* See, for example, *The New York Times*, Sunday, October 6, 1933, p.6.

Charles Rosen.[214] The current abundance of good musicians, and the resulting stiff competition, is why orchestras as well as smaller ensembles have been proliferating and improving for decades, or at least it seems so to me. Instead, I can only conclude that there have been changes in the "wider cultural environment which surrounds classical music."[215] But the related change in demographics has not increased the number of listeners and patrons apace with the number of players.

The cultural environment is in turn affected by changes in the economic environment, especially since the last turn of the century, which has witnessed startling changes, including slowing economic growth that has "devastated American workers," decreased mobility, stifled innovation and entrepreneurial activity, and caused a steep drop in the ownership of businesses, all while the general population ages.[216] Like British culture, ours too is now

> a culture increasingly obsessed with ephemeral celebrity, fed by
> a spin drier of rehashed PR trivia presented as "news," where
> sport is the new religion, where Saturday night fluff like [Dancing with the Stars] is analyzed seriously and given acres of press
> coverage . . . then a cultural landscape invested in supporting all
> that activity damn well ought to have a problem with classical
> music—with its difficultly, with its emotional ambiguity, with
> its allusiveness, with its celebration of individuality, with its refusal to conform, with its ability to move our emotions beyond
> something that can be controlled and manipulated into turning
> a profit."[217]

Almost everyone today listens to (or hears, whether they want to or not) music, usually popular music, every day, and younger generations are very familiar with the pop musicians playing to their generation. We all almost literally exist in a cloud of music. You can mix movements of symphonies and sonatas with Sugababes and Boyzone into a random shuffle on your iPhone in your bathroom or for your commute or morning run, thereby providing wall-to-wall 24/7 background music as you go on with your daily life. An anonymous violinist can serve an identical "free" chaconne to millions of casual listeners while they rack up miles on a treadmill. These activities cost next to nothing, so you don't risk spending time or money on an experience that you may not like.

Younger generations don't always hear music sitting down, and they rarely, as Linus in "Peanuts" confided decades ago to an incredulous Lucy, "just listen to it" (Brahms, in that case). They dance to it, sing to it, drive to it, jog to it. Sitting quietly for hours looking at seventy musicians bowing, blowing, plucking, and pounding just isn't a pleasure they seek, especially those with little listening experience, and with attention spans shortened by TV and digital devices. A classical concert for them may be like being forced to stare for hours at a Cézanne canvas in a museum while knowing little about art, history, or Impressionism—or listening to a lecture delivered in Urdu.

The recent words of conductor Jed Gaylin, while not revelatory, remain generally true: "We need to figure out ways for the potency of great music to reach audiences that admittedly bond, socialize, recreate, and rejuvenate with technologies unforeseen in the era when the symphony orchestra was born."[218] In pondering Gaylin's imperative, I keep these words by Adam Gopnik in mind:

> It isn't a question of classical tastes against pop; it's a question of small forms heard in motion against large forms heard with solemn intent . . . They snatch at music as we snatched at movies, filling our heads with plural images. Music represented for me not the endless, shifting weather-cover of sound that it does for my kids, a cloud in every sense, a perpetual availability of emotion to suit a mood and moment. Music meant difficulty—and, when the difficulty was overcome, the possibilities of life, too. It was something to master.[219]

The problem lies, therefore, in the declining interest in (or market demand for) the products of classical performing artists in our current culture. The challenge is finding ways to get new audience members to and through the doors of concert halls on a more or less regular basis. Approaches to the problem, as I see it, fall into at least three categories: 1) changing the product, 2) improving the marketing of the product, and 3) starting over by priming the pump, exploiting the plasticity of the young developing human brain. All three strategies will need to be called upon in various proportions to suit various local circumstances.

Changing the "Product." A drastic change in the programming of symphony concerts since 1850 needs better understanding and interpretation.[220] Originally, 40 to 50 percent of the works programmed by the New York Philharmonic were written by composers still living. As more than a century and a half passed, however, the proportion of contemporaneous works on concert programs diminished drastically—until, in the 2016–17 season, only 10 percent of programmed works were by living composers, and almost none of them were repeated during the season.

Music directors and conductors choose music for performance or recording with the taste of their audiences (as well as rehearsal time and effort) in mind. Works rediscovered centuries after the death of their classical composers may eventually enter the "canon" and endure for decades or longer, as listener demographics change.* The revival of early music in the 1970s (that brought us Pachebel's "Canon in D") is one example, among others. Should we try to change it? Classical audiences, in general, resist the unknown. That is one characteristic that, especially when measured in decades or centuries, usually distinguishes classical from pop music.

Attempts to change the product—often called "thinking out of the box"—have achieved varying success:

• Enlarging the repertoire. When a serious, accomplished, and thoughtful musician—whether performer or composer or both—offers something new, we shouldn't immediately ask ourselves, "Is it 'classical'?" Speaking for myself, I choose any music that I believe has the potential

* For example, Mendelssohn's *Concerto in d minor for Violin & Piano, MWV 04. T,* re-discovered in 1950.

to be worth my time and effort, whether it is "classical" (meaning what: enduring for longer than some particular time?), "jazz" (played in a jazz club or improvised for the occasion?), or "popular" (listened to by a certain number of people of a certain age?)—or is selected by a respectable curator for a special concert or venue (say, the Ojai Festival, Marlboro, or Gretna Music). Composers like Duke Ellington, George Gershwin, and Dave Brubeck moved easily from Carnegie Hall to jazz clubs in Harlem and Greenwich Village and probably didn't think about what kind of music they were playing. In Ellington's words, "There are only two kinds of music: good music and bad music."

• Changing the contours of the concert: shorter duration, less intimidating ritual and formality, more casual rush-hour or midnight concerts, the Hollywood Bowl, summer music festivals, etc. On occasion I enjoy a shorter concert without intermission.

• Communicating more information about the music played—by means of pre-concert lectures, or musicians talking on stage before playing— on the premise that given increased familiarity with the composer and/or the music, the audience will understand or enjoy the music more and attend more often. That is like fostering fandom. Before each concerto of a performance I attended of Vivaldi's *Four Seasons*, onstage excerpts by the group Apollo's Fire of the many musical representations—of birds, thunder, hunting rifles, teeth chattering, and the like—increased my understanding and enjoyment of this "chestnut" immensely.

• Taking concerts to unconventional places, so that the place itself—a mansion in Newport, caves in Cappadocia, or the forest in Gretna—is an attraction, thereby increasing the incentive to come to enjoy a special experience with friends or family.

• Adding visuals, like costumes or pictures on a screen—to complement the music, just like the smoke and fireworks at Super Bowl musical. (Adding a little sex to a concert is discussed in the next chapter.)

• Providing amenities like restaurants in or near concert halls; wine and snacks at intermission; or meet-the-artist receptions after concerts. The last fosters "fandom" and encourages the sense of a family, in which all share a similar interest.

• Creating programming themes for a group of concerts or an entire season, such as "Mozart and His World" or "The Music of Russia"; and finally

• Keeping classical music vital by always exploring the works of living composers from all over the world, long before those who may eventually be accepted into the canon alongside Beethoven and Brahms are gone.

Improving the *Marketing* of the Product. According to an innovative feedback study by the Austin Ballet and supported by the Wallace Foundation, one new approach to building audiences involves convincing potential concert attendees of a "reasonable certainty that they will enjoy" the music and the evening—a concept they call "bridging the uncertainty gap."[221] The two factors that brought the audience to their concerts were, it turned out: 1) "the social experience of spending time with family and friends" and 2) "the emotional or intellectual reward for experiencing the art itself." And familiarity with the ballet company and its artists presumably helped assure potential audience members that the art they would be experiencing was indeed great art—as opposed to, say, just expensive recreational pleasure.

So finding ways of bridging the uncertainty gap—convincing people that spending a modest amount of time and money on classical music concerts has value for them—may be a path to consider. That is a slightly different strategy from the more typical one of imparting didactic information about the composers' lives, the style or form of the music, the history of the relevant era, or the circumstances of a given work's earlier performances. Rather than trying to convince people that they should or will like Beethoven's music if they know more about Beethoven or his music, providing a professionally filmed good performance on YouTube or Facebook or the like might compete in interest and excitement, at least for some, with Bruno Mars at the Super Bowl. Expanding email campaigns with or without video components are also bearing fruit.

We should also understand and exploit the power of what have come to be called, "social signals." Social media have become an important tool, obviously surpassing print media, in the marketing of culture. The long-held prediction that social media can alter how we choose cultural products has finally come true. Researchers at Microsoft demonstrated that teenagers truly believe that songs downloaded more times are more likely to be worth downloading, even if they did not recognize the songs.[222] When people see what others are downloading, popular songs became "far more popular," and unpopular songs "far less popular," an effect the researchers called "increasing inequality."[223] Such behavior may be a form of social learning (chapter 1), called "copying" when applied to animals and a ubiquitous phenomenon in nature. Copying explains why rats learn to eat only non-poisoned food: They learn by smelling safe food on the coats and breath of healthy rats and detecting traces of previous consumers around the food, thereby obviously enhancing the survival of the species.[224] Similarly, young birds learn birdsongs, and local dialects, from adult tutors. It may not be too much of a leap to assume that a perceived demand for tickets to a performance will increase the actual demand for tickets—and the anticipated value of the experience.

Re-education and Priming the Pump. We might be making a mistake in viewing the classical music problem only as a challenge to improve the product and/or its marketing strategy. It may also relate to a cultural change—driven, in part, by deeper "neurodevelopmental" determinants. President Obama's State of the Union speech in 2013 hinted at this phenomenon. Based on accumulating evidence, he drew a clear connection between what children do in their first decade of life—the earlier, the better—and who they become and what they can do as adults. Inherent in this connection are the concepts of brain plasticity, and critical and sensitive periods in early child development that we've explored in earlier chapters.

The number of applicants to music schools and conservatories seems to have remained stable or even increased over the past several decades. (An influx of immigrants seeking musical education for their children, especially from Asia, may make these numbers difficult to obtain.) The current abundance of good musicians and the resulting stiff competition may be why orchestras and smaller ensembles seem to me to have been improving for decades, at least over my lifetime. And they will, according to the late Charles Rosen, ensure a long, strong future for classical music.[225]

At the same time, the number of people in the pool of audience members has not kept pace with the growing abundance of opportunities to listen to these musicians. As music continues to be withdrawn from American early education and pianos have disappeared from homes, the number of potential audience members who learned music in their living rooms or in grade school but abandoned their early musical skills or transferred them to other, non-musical occupations has probably decreased.

David J. Skorton, MD, cardiologist and new Secretary of the Smithsonian, may agree. "As long as we consider the arts as a frill," he writes, "and as intrinsically less important than learning to code a computer, we're going to systematically disinvest. In school, when something's gotta go, it's art and music."[226] Though unlikely to dissuade students with innate musical talent (and their families) from nurturing that talent outside of schools, that change in educational priorities may rob others of the opportunity for musical education, and they will be less likely to learn the basics—like reading music—and, later, to be part of concert audiences. Continued political attacks on the NEA may worsen this trend.

I discovered music at home in preschool years but was soon nurtured by a good public-school music program, and that was enough for me to want to continue playing music beyond high school. My earliest memories include my mother playing the piano and my father blowing his old trumpet, both instruments untouched since their school years. Now it's clear: They resurrected those skills just for my and my sister's benefit! Neither played well, but how would we know? They also played records: My mother liked "Somewhere Over the Rainbow," my father loved Schubert. My parents knew that imitation is an important form of human social learning. It satisfies an insatiable human search for knowledge, but it is also highly selective: We remain discriminating about what we copy.[227] That imitation "waxes and wanes at an early age and peaks around age four, but never completely disappears, suggests that child-hood imitation also serves a social function—to cement relationships."[228] Absent similar parental guidance, you might find third graders today blasting Jay-Z's "Big Pimpin'" out of their earbuds. Adult participation is clearly desirable.[229] (Alas, imitation may have even more dire conse-quences among a small minority of susceptible viewers of media vio-lence.)

When I was in third grade, after-school home piano lessons inter-rupted my play, but I learned, in fifteen minutes of gently encouraged daily practice, how to make notes printed on a page into tunes, rhythms, and harmonies: my first second language, easy to learn at age eight. After that, math and Latin came easier.

Using my new skills, I could solo with the plastic "flutophone" band by the end of the fourth grade. When I finally picked up a real flute, read-ing and fingering came easy, and I enjoyed being excused from class to play in the small orchestra. In succeeding years, school bands were even more fun. Gentle parental encouragement had become pride, along with admiration at my accomplishments.

Sensitive developmental periods for the brain to acquire skills, like sensorimotor musical skills, as well as aesthetic taste come and go be-fore age nine or ten. We have to learn certain skills while we can. If kids participate only in sports during those years, their future may eventually take them to stadiums rather than concert halls. Though only a handful of my friends continued playing instruments after high school, some of them learned to value the cost of symphony tickets and support their local symphony. And to sing in church.

My parents got as much of a thrill from hearing me play in a school orchestra—because I was good enough—as other parents get from see-ing their sons suit up for the football team. There is a risk, of course, that adults hearing only an average school ensemble will decide they don't like classical music because they have never heard it played well. But some parents clearly do get inspired: Few performances are more exciting than a really good orchestra of kids playing *The Firebird*. As for me, summer music camp at Interlochen instilled the confidence that I could compete successfully with good players and learn a large slice of the repertoire, thereby sealing my fate as a musician and lover of music.

But my musical education was of the traditional kind, based on the understanding that "repetition, standardization, virtuosity, accuracy, perfection, and professionalization (with its emphasis on patterns of conformity) are the terms of our teaching—not experimentation, idiosyncrasy, interaction, individualization, and especially not open-ended creative play." That axiom was attributed to composer Randolph Coleman by Richard Taruskin, who adds, "Mr. Coleman is talking about elite classical-music training, of course, not the less lordly branches of musical life, which have retained far more creativity."[230]

In medical science, single case studies like mine don't prove much but can be educational. My personal example may help explain why at least some members of a symphony audience are in their seats, and might suggest that the decline of music in schools is one reason for classical audiences' dwindling numbers. Imagine the impact of a good orchestral brass quintet or string quartet visiting a third-grade classroom! Maybe not on all kids, but enough of them. Indeed, Peter Dobrin, the critic I quoted above, also advised Philadelphians to conceive of "programs that reach every public school student, regularly, in a serious way."[231]

In contrast, investment in sports, in schools and elsewhere, seems to be increasing as we continue becoming a "shouting culture"[232]: obsessed, after school years, with vicarious watching of sports—and with parents perhaps hoping to see their children excel in ways they did not.

Another advantage of very early music education is suggested by other recent observations: The earlier such education and the higher its quality, the longer an individual is likely to continue music education through college or graduate and professional schools and beyond. That finding may explain data from the NEA: The chance of an adult being in an audience for a classical music concert increases with the duration of that person's education. Those with a graduate school education are nine times more likely to be found at a concert (or, as it happens, in a museum) than those with only a high school diploma. The naive explanation for that observation—that you must be highly educated to appreciate classical music or art—is not well supported. A better explanation may be that if you associate with educated peers, they are more likely to go to—and perhaps invite you to—a classical-music concert than to a tour by the Eagles of Death Metal concert. We can speculate that education, in one or more of a wide variety of different fields, increases our curiosity and initiative to explore what is in the world around us, including the more complex forms of music from the past and present.

Thus, musical ability, on the one hand, and understanding and appreciating complex music on the other—two closely related brain abilities—are best acquired when you are very young and your brain is most sensitive to acquiring many sensorimotor abilities.[233] I am never surprised to learn that a member of our audience played in the school band or sang in a choir, but for various reasons chose a different path from that of a performing musician.

The reality that music education has been jettisoned by cash-poor school boards gives little encouragement that current and future generations will acquire the education that is necessary to understand classical music. If children continue to be denied opportunities during critical and sensitive periods of their lives to learn basic musical skills, acquiring a lifelong love of music will be increasingly unlikely as they get older. Indeed, learning anything may prove more difficult. Nevertheless, an amazing number of the very young somehow seem in time to discover a passion for music. Perhaps that number will even increase in the YouTube era, as chance discoveries by web-surfing three-year-olds lead to, "Mommy I want a violin!" But considering the trends in our culture, they may have to play for each other when they become adults.

The Need for Change. Out of curiosity, I recently attended a flute and piano recital by the faculty of a class of about thirty young flute students—students constitute a majority of the audience at most flute recitals—and came away largely disappointed. The program included the very same late nineteenth-century pieces I had played on flute recitals sixty-five years ago! My assumption was that the teachers thought that their students in the audience would be teaching their students sixty-five years hence how to play the same pieces in the same way. A recipe for the unemployment of a lot of flutists, I thought, and certainly unlikely to capture the interest of many non-flutists. Market forces do apply to music as they do to smartphones.

The world is changing at a pace faster than ever, and music changes with it. Bach's sons realized that the music of their father ("Old Bach") was aging by the day and recognized the need to create new forms and styles. Beethoven's music, now considered "classic," was revolutionary for his time—a time when most performers played the music they had just written; his concert audiences expected new and fresh music. Only later generations of composers, like Brahms and Mahler, began to feel that they were writing for posterity as well as for contemporary audiences. So those of us who insist on playing or hearing only the "classics" are bound to feel that classical music is dying.

We must realize that each generation brings music that is new. Some such will prove ephemeral; some will last—and only those musicians with good "ears" may be able to recognize immediately which is which. The rest of us, like the critic who wrote after the premiere that Tchaikovsky's *Violin Concerto* "stinks to the ear," must keep open minds with respect to new music, and not be put off when it lacks certification as a "classic" in whatever form we might require. That said, however, what makes music "classical" is a timeless quality that allows them to touch listeners over centuries—and our responsibility as lovers of classical music entails the obligation to sustain, contribute to, and nurture possible new additions to the canon that will remain vital for future generations.

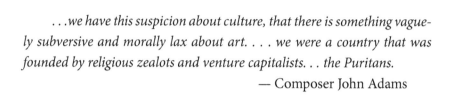

. . .we have this suspicion about culture, that there is something vaguely subversive and morally lax about art. . . . we were a country that was founded by religious zealots and venture capitalists. . . the Puritans.

— Composer John Adams

13
DISDAIN FOR CLASSICAL MUSIC

iscussing his book *Hallelujah Junction: Composing an American Life*, composer John Adams sensed a "suspicious" and "vaguely subversive" view of the arts among the American public.[234] I suspect that such disdain may be felt by a greater portion of Americans than one might expect—though perhaps not surprising in view of the fact that only 55 percent of Americans believe that colleges and universities "have a positive effect on the way things are going in the country."[235] Among Republicans, whom you might assume to be the more avid patrons of the arts,* 58 percent say colleges and universities have a negative effect. Derision and hostility—and perhaps an authoritarian fear of challenge[236]—would seem to constitute a better explanation than budgetary concerns for the current opposition to the national endowments (for the arts and humanities) and the Corporation for Public Broadcasting. We probably should prepare for increasing hostility under what seems likely to be an authoritarian regime that will also threaten academia, science, and medicine as well as free expression in the arts and letters—only partly arising from lack of understanding on the part of people who demand simple answers to complex questions. Wendy Steiner, in *The Scandal of*

---

* For example, David Koch pledged $100 million toward the renovation of the New York State Theater at Lincoln Center and the DeVos family donated $22 million to the Kennedy Center.

Pleasure,[237] and Richard Taruskin, in *The Danger of Music*,[238] address similar issues. James Kennaway discusses yet another threat, music as a pathogen, a threat to manhood, morality, and political order, in *Bad Vibrations. The History of the Idea Of Music as a Cause of Disease.*[239]

People feeling threatened by the arts is nothing new. In the fourth century, St. Augustine wrote in Chapter XXXIII of *The Confessions*: "[W]hen it happens to me to be more moved by the singing than by what is sung, I confess myself to have sinned criminally." In the seventh century, the Prophet Muhammad admonished that "those who listen to music and songs in this world on the Day of Judgment, molten lead will be poured into their ears." And a twelfth-century bishop of Chartres complained regarding the singing in Notre Dame: "Music more easily occasions titillation between the legs than a sense of devotion in the brain."

Craig Monson's *Divas in the Convent*[240] is an abridged version for the general reader of the same author's *Nuns Behaving Badly: Tales of Music, Magic, Art, & Arson in the Convents of Italy*,[241] which, contrary to its risqué title, is actually a scholarly study of sixteenth- and seventeenth-century music and female monasticism. The trouble began in the 1550s, when cloistered singers started to embellish chant (Gregorian and otherwise) with polyphony (singing in parts). The singers were women. Church officials, however, were men, and were more than suspicious. They feared that the nuns would "sing to the world and not to heaven,"[242] and that singing would become an alternative to prayer as a source of pleasure (or, as we learned in chapter 2, as a way to activate their brain reward system and elevate brain dopamine or oxytocin levels). The Master Inquisitor collected testimonies and issued prohibitions, forbidding polyphony and instruments, except for the organ.

Cut to today. One evening last summer, two cousins dropped in to our porch. The waiting line at the local ice cream shop was too long, so they had decided to kill some time with us. They arrived just as three young musicians who had taken showers and dressed in our little downstairs "green room" were carrying instruments to their car for the trip to their concert at the Gretna Playhouse (there are no showers there, and too few dressing rooms) to play the music of Beethoven, Schubert, and Shostakovich.

"We're going to the concert," the cousins said.

Taken aback by their intention to go to a chamber music concert, atypical for these particular cousins, I asked, "The concert?!"

"Yes. We go to the Tabernacle once every summer."

"What's playing there?" I asked.

"Don't know, but we go once every year."

I looked it up in the Gretna Summer Program booklet: There was an old-time group hymn-sing in the nearby Campmeeting Tabernacle.

"Do you like to sing?" I asked.

"No."

"Then I have a proposition for you," I said, as we watched the three young musicians, wearing colorful long silk dresses, drive away. "I'll drive you to our concert in the Playhouse, park right in front, and give you tickets."

The cousins looked at one another uncomfortably: resistance, mixed with irritation. They had never attended a classical-music concert, and never would in their wildest dreams. To avoid further coaxing from me, they quickly thanked us for the lemonade and drove off to the Tabernacle earlier than they had planned.

I sensed actual disdain, which I assume to be fairly common among the general public. I see it on the faces of people passing around the open playhouse during concerts or rehearsals; they would probably not slow their pace, or lower their voices, if they saw Franz Liszt himself at the piano. But I was a little surprised when I saw that on the faces of relatives to whom we regularly extend hospitality.

Of course, I would react similarly if I were invited to a NASCAR race or a tractor pull. And I often do to the suggestion that I attend a concert by one of the loudly amplified cover bands, produced by other Gretna organizations in the playhouse—or some of the painfully loud organ recitals at Emi's St. Margaret's Episcopal Church in Palm Desert, California. Maybe part of my resistance has something to do with my fear of hours of enforced boredom, accompanied by an assault on my declining hearing. I may be forgetting that for some people, a classical concert is like being handcuffed to a chair and having to listen to someone lecture in a foreign language for two hours.

Part of the problem could also relate to circumstances that might have been associated with the results of the November 2016 presidential election: specifically, cultural differences between "coastal" and "heartland" dwellers.[243] (I don't intend to demean the wonderful musical traditions in many parts of the Midwest.) To coastal dwellers, writes Ross Douthat in the *New York Times*, we are a Jeffersonian "propositional nation, bound together by ideas rather than [by] any specific cultural traditions." (Jefferson, as it happened, both loved and played music.) They feel they are part of "a nation of immigrants drawn to Ellis Island, a nation of minorities claiming rights too long denied, a universal nation destined to welcome foreigners and defend liberty abroad." And after all, classical music was brought to the U.S. mostly by immigrants, relatively recently, and mostly by Europeans, some of them driven from their homes. Now, in part attracted by these same immigrants and their students, Asian immigrants populate the expanding pool of classical musicians and classical music listeners. Classical music players and listeners regularly cross many boundaries and oceans.

In contrast, heartland dwellers embrace a "settler" rather than "immigrant" culture, Anglo-Saxon and Protestant, that demands "assimilation to its norms." Their "great national drama was a westward expansion that conquered a native population rather than coexisting with it... They still embrace the Iliadic mythos that grew up around the Civil War, [and] prefer the melting pot to multiculturalism..."[244] Settler culture finds comfort and security in convention and tradition and mistrusts change in the form of innovation, and especially artistic freedom. Its members may resent the fact that their tax money is used to support the National Endowment for the Arts, exponentially overestimating the actual amount of federal spending—0.004 percent of the federal budget, less than the cost of a year's expenses for the current first lady to live in New York—because they believe it goes toward pleasing only the elite.

Another, more ominous, consideration was raised in a recent *New York Times* Op-Ed piece by Eve Ewing.

But as Hitler understood, artists play a distinctive role in challenging authoritarianism. Art creates pathways for subversion, for political understanding and solidarity among coalition builders. Art teaches us that lives other than our own have value. Like the proverbial court jester who can openly mock the king in his own court, artists who occupy marginalized social positions can use their art to challenge structures of power in ways that would otherwise be dangerous or impossible. . . . We need the arts because they make us full human beings. But we also need the arts as a protective factor against authoritarianism. In saving the arts, we save ourselves from a society where creative production is permissible only insofar as it serves the instruments of power. When the canary in the coal mine goes silent, we should be very afraid—not only because its song was so beautiful, but also because it was the only sign that we still had a chance to see daylight again.[245]

Back to the cousins. Our concert by the Trio Terzetto was exquisite. The audience, here in rural Pennsylvania Dutch heartland countryside— the audience—stood and cheered.

As Paul Krugman said about behavior in our government, even before it became totally insane: "I don't fully understand it, but it's a terrible thing to behold." I could try to write some lofty words about arts and culture, but they have all been said before and will be said again as plans go forward for defunding the National Endowments for the Arts and Humanities and the Corporation for Public Broadcasting. At least some of us will keep trying to keep alive "the better angels of our nature," and will take heart from the fact that new Mozarts will continue to come along with every new generation, though there may be fierce disagreement about who they are. This divide is nothing new. It existed in Bach's Leipzig:

It is but a pity that in such a famous place, where the muses
have taken up their seat, there are at the same time so few con-
noisseurs and lovers of true music.

— Lorenz Christoph Mizler (1747),
as cited by John Eliot Gardner[246]

Without a song . . . there ain't no love at all
— Billy Rose and Edward Eliscu

[B]etween "reality" on the one hand, and the point where the mind strikes reality, there's a middle zone, a rainbow edge where beauty comes into being, where two very different surfaces mingle and blur to provide what life does not: and this is the space where all art exists, and all magic. . . . And — I would argue as well — all love.
— Donna Tartt, *The Goldfinch*

14
Love: A Neuromusical Rhapsody

From Shakespeare's "thy sweet love remembered such wealth bring" to "I ♡ My Labradoodle," "love" is an overused word. "Love you," as we say goodbye to a friend. "Give her my love." "Love your necklace!" "I'd love to," in response to an invitation. "I love you," from the read lips of a diva throwing kisses to a raving audience. Google "love" for 4.6 trillion more examples! One might come to believe there is more love in our world than there actually is.

The word defies definition. Dictionaries suggest affection more intense than the equally familiar word "like." I like Justice Potter Stewart's work-around: "I know it when I see it" (applied to a more problematic word), but I haven't always been correct in my own love life. It makes sense to break up a broad concept into manageable pieces. Ancient Greeks worshipped an Olympian goddess, Aphrodite, who with her companion, Eros, embodied erotic love as well as beauty, pleasure, and procreation. The Greek word a*gápē* signified universal transcendent love between god(s) and mankind, while *philēo* expressed brotherly love. For many observers, love has a purely spiritual source uninfluenced by external social realities. St. Paul (1 Corinthians 13) considered love to be God's spiritual gift to humans: "And now abide faith, hope, love, these three; but the greatest of these is love."

Poets may have had the best chance of successfully expressing a defi-nition in words. Sappho (621?–570 BCE) may have begun the enterprise with her unique performance art that combined song, dance, and poetry in ways that will always remain a mystery because it only happened live, usually in the service of preparing young people for love and living, and then disappeared to posterity:

Exquisite Eros I'll not neglect,
I'll praise him, garlanded, flower-decked,
who over gods maintains his sway,
as over creatures of a day.

Like a smith —
again Love strikes the hammer's blow,
plunging me
in winter's torrent as I glow.[247]

—Sappho

And consider:

Love is anterior to life,
    Posterior to death,
Initial of creation, and
    The exponent of breath.

— Emily Dickinson

Extinguish my eyes, I'll go on seeing you.
Seal my ears, I'll go on hearing you.
And without feet I can make my way to you,
without a mouth I can swear your name.

Break off my arms, I'll take hold of you
with my heart as with a hand.
Stop my heart, and my brain will start to beat.
And if you consume my brain with fire,
I'll feel you burn in every drop of my blood.

— Rainer Maria Rilke

Indeed, what has shaped our concept of love most strongly over the centuries has been art. "It is through novels, poems, songs and, latterly, films that we have acquired our ideas about what aspects of our feelings we should value and where our emotional emphases should fall," writes Alain de Botton. [248] "This is unfortunate," he continues. "It's not that the art has been bad; indeed a lot of it has reached the highest aesthetic pitch. It's simply that representations of love in culture have frequently been profoundly misleading at the psychological level." Too bad, he muses, that Madame Bovary could not have read Flaubert's novel before she decided her marriage was humdrum and began her ultimately fatal flings.

Part of the problem could be that scientists have yet to discover how to measure love, though we can quantify memory and intelligence and blood pressure. Can we use the duration of a kiss? The eloquence of a love letter? Fervor measured in kilowatt hours? In dark moods, I may think that the truest love will be revealed by the one who comforts me when I'm dying. Psychologists use the word "limerence" to stand for an almost instantaneous but short-lasting bloom of infatuation that eventually fades—"Tuca Tuca," in the words of the band Pink Martini[249]—often leaving in its wake all sorts of problems. Even long-lasting love seems to vary in quality and apparent intensity over a lifetime. Love eludes a clinical definition as well as measurement.

Scientists *can* measure endorphins, the hormone oxytocin, and the brain neurotransmitters serotonin and dopamine—chemicals that mediate emotional experiences such as pleasure in close relationships. They flow among pleasure regions in the brain: the ventral tegmental area, the nucleus accumbens, and the insula—the same parts of the brain most affected by addictive drugs. We are beginning to understand the biology of love, but none of these measurements help much to understand how love functions in daily life—and certainly not how to control it in ourselves when we are struck.

Music, in pathways parallel to language, activates similar neural networks in the brain and stimulates the same neurotransmitters and hormones as love and other pleasures. Ancient Greek actors *sang* their tragedies to enhance the emotional impact of the stories they told. Among recent Metropolitan Opera productions, Donizetti's *Roberto Devereux* demonstrated the awesome power of love—love is indeed "playing with fire," both in its needed and welcoming heat as well as in its power to destroy—and showed how music can help express that power. Franz Schubert and Robert Schumann knew this, as did other composers, including Gustav Mahler: "With songs one can express so much more than the words directly say. . . . The text actually constitutes only a hint of the deeper content that is to be drawn out of it, of the treasure that is to be hauled up." The "Song to the Moon" in *Rusalka* and "*S'io non moro a quest accenti*" in *Idomeneo* are only two of thousands of examples that prove Mahler's point. The Met's *Elektra* used the awesome power of music to bring an ancient tragedy back to new life after thousands of years, one that remains truly hair-raising to humans living now.

Love is rarely more powerful than when it is lost, through death or by leaving or being left. The great Stoic philosopher Epictetus (c. 55—135 AD) wrote:

Who is good if he knows not who he is? And who knows what he is. If he forgets that things which have been made are perishable, and that it is not possible for one human being to be with another always?*

From a letter I was once saddened to receive:

[T]here is no way in the world that one can talk, sing or write about love without facing the powerful element of loss that is inherent in loving someone, as well as the everlasting hold it has on one when that love is joyful and connected, profound and caring, and passionate, which is what I feel for you. It is something I am unwilling to give up just yet, which creates its own

---

* Quoted by Maria Popova, *Epictetus on Love and Loss: The Stoic Strategy for Surviving Heartbreak*, https://mailchimp/brainpickings/epictetus-neruda-water?e=81c44f77ff

dilemma given the complete uncertainty of our lives. . . .

Music can also be a sexual stimulant, though you may argue that some contemporary performers go beyond civilized limits to arouse pubescent fourteen-year-olds who are still in the process of developing lifelong musical tastes and identities. Sonos and Apple companies (certainly not disinterested investigators, but their work was peer-reviewed by musical psychologist Dan Levitin) claim that couples who spend time listening to live or recorded music together make love more frequently than those who listen in solitude through earbuds. Wall-to-wall music in homes, they further claim, makes entire families happier.[250] (It usually irritates or distracts me, though.)

And think of it: Music on stage synchronizes the brain activity of all of us sitting together in the audience! Pianist Vijay Iyer observes: "In my own experience playing for audiences, synchronization is the primary force that I feel is at work—the sense that we're all in our room experiencing this together."[251] Your mind might wander to the "Furtwängler concerts": broadcasts in 1944 Germany featuring the music of German masters—Bruckner, Beethoven, Wagner—and heard simultaneously by both the "free" German people and inmates of Buchenwald through the camp public address system. And I think of violinist Szymon Laks in Auschwitz: "When an esman [SS man] listened to music, especially of the kind he really liked, he somehow became similar to a human being."[252]

Coachella is certainly a place to see live music . . . [253]

15

Sex and Classical Music

Better Marketing Through Chemistry

A typical discussion about how classical music can regain the interest of the American public usually goes on about making concerts relevant, accessible, casual, non-threatening, and affordable, plus adding gimmicks and marketing strategies to drag the dusty old classics into the twenty-first century and younger generations into the halls. How about bird feathers floating down over the audience after the cannons in the *1812 Overture*?

But one element I don't hear so much about is sex—maybe because older audiences are reticent to talk about it. What most younger Americans call "concerts" are loaded with sexual energy. Go to livenation.com, think Beyoncé, Lady Gaga, Bruno Mars, Pit Bull, or any bare-chested guitarist holding the neck of his instrument.

Bruce Springsteen told The New Yorker's David Remnick, "I want an extreme experience!" And he wants his audience to leave the arena "with your hands hurting, your feet hurting, your back hurting, your voice sore, and your sexual organs stimulated!"[254] And the pop/rock singer Ben Folds, talking with Allison Babka about his occasional concerts with orchestras, insisted "[i]t's the best place to take anyone on a date. It's perfect. It's not loud as shit, you're not talking over each other, you're seated and you can make a move under the program sheet."

"People," Folds exclaims, "This will get you laid."[255]

Whoa!

The interviewer subsequently added: "Ben Folds was very passionate about the orchestra's ongoing role in society… and he'll tell you things in a very colorful manner…he's inspired by the symphony, he's passionate about quality music and he's honored to perform with so many gifted musicians…I think Folds has proven …that the right combination of pop and classical can appeal to many demographics and entice newer, younger audiences to give the orchestra a try…"[256]

Hardly measuring up to this raw carnality is the subtle eroticism of Ravel's "La Flûte Enchantée" in *Shéhérazade*, or the "Song to the Moon" in Dvořák's *Rusalka*, or Debussy's *Prélude à l'après-midi d'un faune*. These can put to sleep any youngster, even the most hormonally besotted, though the latter two were composed to accompany "visuals"—an opera in one case and a symphonic poem, later a dance, in the other—with strong sexual content. In "La Flûte," the sexual content must be imagined—not easy, perhaps, for those used to seeing it made explicit in almost every song and who don't read books.

There may be some hope for change on the horizon, however. Writing about the young pianist Yuja Wang, Janet Malcolm observed in *The New Yorker*:

> As she performed, the thigh, splayed by the weight of the torso
> and the action of the toe working the pedal, looked startlingly
> large, almost fat, though Yuja is a very slender woman. Her
> back was bare, thin straps crossing it. She looked like a domina-
> trix or a lion tamer's assistant. She had come to tame the beast
> of a piece, this half-naked woman in sadistic high heels. Take
> that, and that, Beethoven![257]

So, music need not be, as Emily Dickinson said, "invisible." Malcolm continues:

> She is keenly aware—as many soloists affect not to be—that she

is being looked at as well as listened to. Reviewing the Carnegie Hall recital Yuja played in May, 2013, Zachary Woolfe wrote in the Times, "I confess that while perhaps 90 percent of my attention was on her precise yet exuberant playing, a crucial 10 was on her skintight flame-colored dress." Woolfe went on to brilliantly anatomize the experience of simultaneously listening to and looking at Yuja: "Her alluring, surprising clothes don't just echo the allure and surprise of her musicianship, though they certainly do that. More crucial, the tiny dresses and spiky heels draw your focus to how petite Ms. Wang is, how stark the contrast between her body and the forcefulness she achieves at her instrument. That contrast creates drama. It turns a recital into a performance." When Yuja played the "Jeunehomme" in the girlish pink dress, that contrast was absent. The sense of a body set in urgent motion by musical imperatives requires that the body not be distractingly clothed. With her usually bared thighs, chest, and back demurely covered by the black-splotched pink fabric, this sense was lost.

♫

The great nineteenth-century Hungarian virtuoso pianist Franz Liszt nurtured an international rock star–like reputation for erotic conquest, cultivating the image of a Don Juan. He exploited his dazzling, "transcendental" (his word) virtuosity as a representation of sexual domination, and women fought over his snuff-box and cigar butts and pieces of his handkerchief. His piano fantasy "Réminiscences of Don Giovanni" could thus be considered a self-portrait, just as everyone had assumed that Byron's *Don Juan* was autobiographical.

Liszt's invention, the piano recital by one person alone, was indeed a performance, foreshadowing Bruce Springsteen by more than a century. Liszt was the nineteenth century's greatest piano virtuoso and arguably the greatest such who ever walked the planet. Yet, bathed in controversy ever since his birth in 1811, Liszt earned both the respect and contempt of Robert and Clara Schumann, Chopin, and Brahms, who all accused him (and his son-in-law, Richard Wagner) of vulgar showmanship, contrary to their view that music should be played only for its own sake. Clara wrote in her marriage diary, "I am convinced that the reason Liszt displays such arrogance at times is really the fault of the women, because they pay court to him everywhere in a way that is intolerable to me and that I find highly improper." Liszt even tried to flirt with Clara.[258] But Liszt's detractors were awestruck by his ability and perhaps jealous of it, and would probably agree that Liszt could make his Chickering piano* do just as much as anyone will ever be able to do on any piano, even a modern Steinway.

Many might agree with Charles Rosen:

> *The harmonics can be banal, the melodies almost nonexistent… In some of the Hungarian Rhapsodies, there is zero degree of musical invention if we insist that invention must consist of melody, rhythm, harmony, and counterpoint. Nevertheless, played with a certain elegance, these are both dazzling and enchanting. The real invention concerns texture, density, tone color, and intensity—the various noises that can be made with a piano —and it is startlingly original. The piano was taught to make new sounds. These sounds often did not conform to an ideal of beauty, either Classical or Romantic, but they enlarged the meaning of music, made possible new modes of expression. On a much larger scale, Liszt did for the piano what Paganini had done for the violin. Listeners were impressed not only with the beauty of Paganini's tone quality but also with its occasional ugliness and brutality, with the way he literally attacked his instrument for such dramatic effect. Liszt made a new range of dramatic piano sound possible, and in so doing thoroughly overhauled the technique of keyboard playing.*[260]

---

* The piano was a gift from the widow of Liszt's Hungarian friend, Baron Antal Augusz. Chickering had a patent (1840-43) on its cast-iron frame which gave the instrument a greater stability and a richer sound.[259]

Liszt exploited not only virtuosity but also a satanic public image and a Gothic taste for the macabre with all its paraphernalia: dances of death and the like. He was also a virtuoso conductor, doing more than anyone else in his time (except maybe Berlioz) to create the modern image of the orchestra conductor as an international star. He invented the symphonic "tone poem" (like *Les Préludes*) and was the first composer to write atonal (or, at least, harmonically audacious) music, foreshadowing Debussy and Schoenberg. Liszt was a scrupulous editor or arranger of the works of other composers—and also a borrower of their themes.

♫

A researcher at the University College of London, Chia-Jung Tsay, studies how we evaluate a performance of music.[261] What makes us consider a performance great, or not? Tsay's results confirm the idea that, when we respond to and evaluate a performance of music, we use our eyes as well as our ears! Tsay selected two groups of subjects, each numbered in the hundreds: One group consisted of professional musicians and the other of just plain folks (which is to say, musical novices). Tsay shared with them performances by: 1) a highly ranked ("world-class") orchestra, say the Chicago Symphony, and 2) an average regional orchestra, say a fictitious Fargo Philharmonic. Each performance was six seconds long and was experienced three times: by means of a) a sound recording, b) a silent video recording, and c) a recording with audio *and* video, all of the same passage in the music.

Subjects also were exposed to performances by chamber ensembles: prize-winning vs. just average ones. Tsay described in great detail her experimental methods, and her statistical evaluation of the results of dozens of separate tests. Her assessments seem rigorous and complete to me. She had to make sure that none of her subjects got any clues to the right answers to her single question: Which of the two performances in each test was by the supposedly higher-rated, professional ensemble?

To oversimplify the results for clarity: The only times significant numbers of either group of subjects identified the prestigious ensembles correctly (more frequently than by chance) were *when they viewed the silent video performances*! Even the musician subjects couldn't distinguish a Fargo Philharmonic from a Chicago Symphony from a six-second sound recording alone! One additional subtest also produced similar results (i.e., the subjects chose the professionals correctly) when the silent video recording narrowly focused on the one member of an ensemble who appeared to be the de facto leader of the ensemble. When the camera focused on the "followers," the subjects' responses were no better than chance.

There is more detail in the report, but all of the results followed this same pattern and was supported by robust statistics. As in all research, insightful critics can often discover hidden bias that could change the results and conclusions. And as in all research, someone else needs to repeat the experiments and confirm or deny these results. My criticism would be that I need longer than six seconds of music to make any judgment about it. But these results are nevertheless consistent with my reaction to many orchestra concerts: Any behavior of the players that indicates their intense, sincere commitment to the music—say the entire second violin section moving like a wave in sync with the music—enhances my response to the music. Try looking at an Abbado performance (on DVD) of Mahler with his Lucerne Festival Orchestra, with the sound turned off.

As with all good research, the results of this study raise additional questions. Will rankings ("likes"?) of recordings change as more people experience music on YouTube than on audio recordings? What are the implications for those of us who champion live music in the "mp3 era"? Should we re-evaluate the most recent policy of auditioning candidates for orchestras behind screens? (Tsay doesn't mention that that policy began when "old white men" conductors had certain biases—surprisingly, against women!) Should music schools change their teaching methods? Are the "best" orchestra conductors ranked that way on account of their appearance?—and have the people who make music videos known this for years? At least now I understand the success of the smiling André Rieu, who regularly appears with violin and happy orchestras during PBS fund-raising season!

Maybe we know now why the very *un*sexy Glenn Gould abandoned live performances in favor of recordings and radio broadcasts, claiming that to see the performer was a distraction from the musical experience.

I never meant to cause you any sorrow
I never meant to cause you any pain
I only wanted to one time to see you laughing
I only wanted to see you
Laughing in the purple rain.

—Prince

16
'Purple Brain' (2016)

Prince's unexpected tragic death (last week, as I write this), caused me try to recall what planet I lived on when Prince (Rogers Nelson, born June 7, 1958) burst onto the earth. Before last week, if someone had mentioned "Purple Rain," I would have imagined some kind of climate aberration. In 1983 I was trying to survive as a medical professor, and was celebrating the fact that Gretna Music had just signed Dave Brubeck, Marian McPartland, and members of the Chicago Symphony to our summer concert schedule. I was, obviously, oblivious when Prince appeared as a distant star at, or beyond, the far edge of my universe.

Until last week, I could not have named any of the songs that have become, also outside of my awareness, cultural treasures, known to more humans than the combined songs of Schubert, Schumann, Mahler, and maybe even Walt Disney. My aging ears can't even understand the words of these songs. The repeated video clips celebrating Prince's life are all new and strange to me.

As with his friendly rival, Michael Jackson, fans were attracted as much, or more, to Prince's performances than to his music alone—at least it seems that way to me. The music sounds to me like most other rock music: uncomfortably loud; harmonically, lyrically, and rhythmically simple; repetitive; self-referential; opaquely arranged; and to my ears frankly uninteresting, regardless of the singer's four-octave range, from deep bass to an impossibly high falsetto. "Not the prettiest instrument, but he was very musical, as in, expressive... a growl or a whisper... his African rhythms stripped of their Puritan sensibility," according to one adoring fan.

That fan saw Prince as "subversive, hedonistic, provocative, excessive" in most of his stage behavior, appearing in "gender-bending clothes, not only masculine but sexy, at least to a lot of women I know, including me...There was a mischief about him, a playfulness, even as he sang things that made me blush...I saw the 'Rude Boy' pin, a Jamaican phrase for gangsters, combined with the pompadour, eye makeup, and those lovely doe eyes."[262]

The costumes and prancing around were apparently more than the usual angry, aggressive, preening male strutting of rock singers—all necessary, I assume, to hold the attention of younger generations who probably couldn't find middle C on a piano. It's more about performance, and social commentary, than music, but I suppose it's one way to interest teenagers in music.

But wait! Is that very different from opera? Did I miss an important and perhaps revolutionary development in music in my lifetime? Was Prince an example of new and valid music, and possibly a genius? During his generation, recordings changed from sound-alone CDs to video-and-sound DVDs, and the Metropolitan Opera and many orchestras began live video broadcasts.

I wish I had paid more attention to his work and learned to understand it and know him better as a songwriter, musician, and person. I am embarrassed that my behavior is exactly what I have criticized in others—in particular, the tendency to arbitrarily categorize music made by humans, confine my listening to just one or two categories, and dismiss others as not worthy of my time.

So why don't I understand Prince? Dan Levitin, musical psychologist, says:

Fourteen is a sort of magical age for the development of musical tastes. Pubertal growth hormones make everything we're experiencing, including music, seem very important. We're just reaching a point in our cognitive development when we're developing our own tastes. And musical tastes become a badge of identity.[263]

At age fourteen, I was playing Franz von Suppé's *Poet and Peasant Overture* and John Philip Sousa's *The Thunderer* march in my junior high school band. I heard some pop music—Patti Page, Eddie Fisher, Les Paul and Mary Ford—but only as background to my other busy pre-driver's-license adolescent interests, like basketball and model airplanes. By the time rock 'n' roll arrived—Bill Haley and the Comets, Chuck Berry—I was sixteen and found it rather curious and comical, given that I was learning to play Brahms and Dvorak symphonies and Stravinsky's *Firebird* in the orchestra at Interlochen. Years later, when Prince arrived, my musical tastes had long been set, and my brain was less receptive to new kinds of music. Maybe if I had taken more time to understand him, I would have had a fuller life afterward. Others close to me and to my age have suggested as much.

PART TWO
REFLECTIONS ON A MUSICAL LIFE

Interlochen changed my life.

— any one of 120,000 alumni

17
A Model for Arts Education

More than once as I've slowed my car to turn into the Interlochen gates, I've noticed, just feet from my rear window, massive bumpers and headlights belonging to pickups driven by impatient drivers, most likely towing a brace of jet skis or dirt bikes. As I turned, they roared past, jeering and displaying derisive hand gestures that date back to ancient Greece. Their drivers resented me, an effete artsy person delaying their vacation at the state park that shares the isthmus between two lakes with the Interlochen Center for the Arts (further evidence, perhaps of disdain for classical music).

But once through the new gates (required by Homeland Security, I was told), I've felt comfortable and secure in a place I had called home for ten summers decades ago. The blue lakes, towering pines, and cacophony of music from every direction are my concept of heaven. Where else could you hear one high school orchestra rehearsing Mussorgsky with your left ear and another playing Brahms with your right while alternating your view between the dedicated kids on stage and sailboats skimming across the lake beyond?

The venerable ninety-year-old Interlochen Center for the Arts has just selected a new president, the first in fourteen years, to guide the institution in its mission statement: "to inspire people worldwide through excellence in educational, artistic and cultural programs, enhancing the quality of life through the universal language of the arts"—or, as founder Joseph E. Maddy wrote as the Great Depression approached:

> *…to develop and enhance the mental, intellectual and creative capacities of our nation's young people, to bring forth their innate potentialities, to prepare them for the cultural, intellectual and moral leadership so necessary for this nation's survival.* *

My ten summers at Interlochen accomplished both versions of that mission for me—at least the parts about enhancing capacities and bringing forth innate potentialities, not to mention acquiring life-long friendships. The experience definitely shaped my life more than any other, excepting perhaps my education at Yale Medical School.

Interlochen's mission has become even more critical in today's world, I think, though the country (and beyond) is surely a better place because of the presence of more than 120,000 other Interlochen alumni. The school claims that it has educated players occupying 17 percent of the chairs in American orchestras. Its graduates possess hundreds of Tony and Grammy awards, and serve in other occupations as well—including doctors, lawyers, Goldman Sachs directors, professors and teachers, and many more. Early music and arts education helps prepare kids for almost anything.

Interlochen nurtures children as young as third graders in a creative artistic environment, guided by capable and caring people, at a time in their lives when they are most creative and receptive to learning music, languages, and many other skills. (As I said in chapter 3, college age is too late to decide to become a musician and develop the extensive sensorimotor brain hardware required.) About twenty-five hundred students come each summer, from all fifty states and more than fifty countries, for the opportunity to develop proficiency and nurture creativity in all the arts and literature—disciplines that have been withdrawn from many public schools, and are often not present any longer in many homes, either. They make friends and learn to live together. Imagine how it feels

* Interlochen archives

when all your school friends value making music, art, dance, drama, and poetry as much as prowess in tackling one another on the football field. The competition is just as keen, but the qualities and skills gained last a lifetime.

The Interlochen environment, both natural—twelve hundred wooded acres between two large glacial lakes—and human, is crucial. Students play in orchestras conducted by some of world's best conductors, like JoAnn Falletta (or, in the past, John Phillip Sousa). A concertmaster of a major orchestra, like Martin Chalifour of the Los Angeles Philharmonic, may join them in the violin section. They accompany soloists like Van Cliburn (in my era) or Yo-Yo Ma and study their instruments and chamber music with artists like flutist Paula Robison. They see, and act in, Shakespeare plays; attend dance concerts by the Martha Graham Company; and meet authors, poets, and composers (like Howard Hanson or Aaron Copland). Among the thousand-strong staff and faculty, role models are limitless and diverse. A cabin counselor may be a band director or a jazz pianist; an aspiring writer, painter, or filmmaker; or a Broadway singer. The server in the cafeteria line or the lifeguard may be a clarinetist or an actor. All of these people are potential mentors and possible lifelong friends. Students hear their

Fig. 5. Lakefront of the Interlochen Center for the Arts. Kresge Hall and Dance Building to the left

teachers and colleagues and perform for and with one another. Parents or grandparents may have been campers or winter students in years past; some may even be working on campus.

During the school year, the Interlochen Arts Academy, a boarding high school made possible through the generosity of the rags-to-riches insurance magnate W. Clement Stone (who himself had dropped out of school), distills and intensifies all these activities for five hundred high school students in a similar, albeit cooler, environment. The academy graduated forty-three presidential scholars, almost one each year. Interlochen Public Radio broadcasts news and information from one station and classical music and jazz from another to a large part of northern Michigan. The College of Creative Arts offers continuing education for adults, and Interlochen Presents, a performing arts series, stages hundreds of student, faculty, and professional performances and exhibits each year.

Interlochen is a nonprofit corporation with an annual operating budget of more than $40 million and an endowment valued at $120 million, but the culture is anything but corporate. It does not exist to financially enrich stockholders or executives; rather, all the stakeholders of Interlochen aim to enrich the lives of younger generations, and thus the lives of all of us. Board members are not paid, and some faculty and staff accept less than usual financial compensation in return for the opportunity to just be there and participate. Interlochen is a Chautauqua (described in chapter 18)* for young people, in the generic sense of an oasis, where the best qualities of younger generations of humanity are nurtured and protected during critical developing years, away from the frightening, polarized, "open carry" society around it. That environment is made and tended by hundreds of people, all with different backgrounds, talents, and responsibilities, as well as distinctive history and memories. Not surprisingly, loyalty to Interlochen probably surpasses that to most other institutions of its kind. Its 120,000 alumni make up a vast and growing generous resource for sustaining and pro-

* "Chautauqua" is the Iroquois name of a lake in New York, as Interlochen's two lakes were named "Wahbekaness" and "Wahbekanetta" by Native American Odawa people.

moting this unique environment.*

The Interlochen environment, however, is also fragile and easily disturbed. Its leaders need to be assertive and forceful in maintaining and advancing Interlochen's place in a world increasingly unfriendly to the Interlochen mission. At the same time, the Interlochen environment itself needs to be protected by those leaders, so that they are both facing outwards, as effective, sometimes ruthless corporate executives, and inward, as caring, listening, supportive leaders of a large family, enabling all to achieve their greatest potential. They carefully and sensitively replenish the institution with new people and ideas while trying to increase the diversity of the student body, so that opportunities to share the Interlochen experience are provided for as many socioeconomic levels of younger generations as possible.

* For a humorous account of one former summer camper's experience, see Thom Feild, Pine Nuts: Recollections of Summers at Interlochen (Thom Feild Design LLC, 2006).

Never was the shade
Of a tree
More delightful
And cherished.

— "Ombra mai fù," aria from *Serse*
Georg Friedrich Händel

18

THERE'S NO PLACE
LIKE MT. GRETNA

Shortly after I moved in 1973 to Mt. Gretna, Pennsylvania—attracted by real estate less expensive than in nearby Hershey, where Penn State's new medical center gave me my first job—I took a walk through its narrow winding streets and hillside paths, lined with the porches of quaint nineteenth-century cottages. Because my first visit to the region, for house-hunting, had lasted only one weekend, I was astonished to see my new neighborhood, around the house I had so hastily bought. Streets and paths were like tunnels under a thick canopy of pine and oak trees.

After passing a small lake and tennis courts, I came upon a round wooden outdoor auditorium with a roof like an umbrella, supported by posts around its edges and filled with benches facing a small stage. It was surrounded on three sides by cottages, some only a few feet away. A faded sign read: "Chautauqua Playhouse." Rustling sounds suggested that birds or bats were nesting high in the complex network of open trusses supporting the conical roof. Broken slats on the benches gave evidence of juvenile mischief, and piles of sawdust at the base of eighteen large chestnut posts reflected a year's work on the part of small boring beetles. As I emerged from the auditorium's dark interior, I was able to see, ghostlike through the trunks of trees, several more nineteenth-century wooden

Chautauqua buildings, all with faded pale-yellow siding, some with tall wooden columns, all right in my neighborhood. I was later saddened to learn that the old Chautauqua Inn nearby had been demolished just two years before, as the majestic Conewago Hotel, overlooking a lake, had been thirty years earlier—the first hotel in the area, they say, to have offered a private bath with every bedroom and live music with dining.

Originally, these buildings on the side of a forested hill had awaited visitors who, like President Benjamin Harrison in 1890, arrived by train along a branch line through miles of cornfields connecting the manufacturing cities of Lebanon and Lancaster. As a senator from Indiana in

Fig. 6, The Mt. Gretna Playhouse

the 1880s, Harrison had introduced several bills to designate the Grand Canyon as a "public park," without success. Later, as president, he succeeded in making it a forest preserve. Whether he had similar designs for Mt. Gretna may never be known.

Other visitors came in summers to frolic in a small forest amusement park, listen to preachers and choirs, and swim or canoe in a man-made pond hardly large enough to justify its name, Lake Conewago. That name dubiously honored the tribe of original forest inhabitants—who, I presume, had fled when loggers arrived to cut fuel for the Iron Furnace in nearby Cornwall that forged cannons for George Washington's army. Over a hundred years later, residents dammed a small creek to create the pond that increased recreational opportunities and supplied ice for the sparse population, for hotels, and for an adjacent National Guard summer encampment—and for skating. As decades passed, the soldiers moved away to a larger space, and automobiles made it easier for vacationers to drive to more exotic places. The railway was abandoned (eventually to become, now, a popular "rail-to-trail"), and Mt. Gretna quietly settled back into the deepening forest during the World Wars and the Great Depression.

I was familiar with the Iroquois word "Chautauqua" because my grandmother spent summers at the original Chautauqua Institution in New York State. Two Methodists started the New York community in 1874, alongside another lake with an Indian name and along another railroad. It remains one of the few still existing, dedicated to

> *the exploration of the best in human values and the enrichment*
> *of life through a program that explores the important religious,*
> *social and political issues of our times; stimulates provocative,*
> *thoughtful involvement of individuals and families in creative*
> *response to such issues; and promotes excellence and creativity*
> *in the appreciation, performance and teaching of the arts.*[264]

The Pennsylvania Chautauqua, established in 1892 with a similar intent and into which I had serendipitously moved, contains about two hundred homes on one-seventh of a square mile, within a larger, indefinitely bordered concentration of houses, trees, and small businesses loosely referred to as "the Mt. Gretna area." It compares in scale and population to its sibling in New York, much as our ten-acre Lake Conewago does to the twenty-square-mile Lake Chautauqua. With a few notable exceptions, like ours and the one in New York, the Chautauqua movement and its physical traces have been squeezed to the edge of existence by college summer schools, more attractive recreational places, and changing mobility and demographics, leaving only old Victorian-style buildings, fading memories, and antiquarian anthologies. The word might survive as a generic name for "a place for quiet, thoughtful inquiry," as it is invoked in *Zen and the Art of Motorcycle Maintenance*—though that concept might be disappearing from modern life, too.

In July 1976, theater productions in the Chautauqua Playhouse had gone dark for the first time since 1927 because of squabbles over the rent. A few friends and I raked leaves off the bare earth from under the splintered benches in the vacant place: a damp, termite-infested wooden shell first built in 1894 and rebuilt eight years later after a fire. The backstage area was littered with old sets and trash. We replaced the four bare light bulbs high above the stage and set up kitchen chairs and music stands for the first concert of what our poster announced in large Roman letters:

MUSIC AT GRETNA

above the now iconic bass in the woods drawn by the artist Bruce Johnson, who lived up the hill. Smaller letters listed the players, some from the Pittsburgh Symphony, and added, "Donation, $3.00, children $1.00."

I didn't imagine that that year would be the first year of decades of music. I simply wanted to play with musicians I could choose, like those I had known at Interlochen and the Eastman School (and those in the Audubon Quartet; their story in chapter 23). As with tennis, playing music with good, serious players is far more satisfying.

Almost mysteriously, an audience appeared, and the four chamber music concerts of our first summer came up against a timeless local tradition: "Let's do it again next year!" (An exasperating tradition only when "exactly the same way" is appended.) The musicians enthusiastically agreed, though they had been paid only with hospitality. In 1977, supported by a grant from the Pennsylvania Council on the Arts, we increased the number of concerts and added jazz, and by year five an article in *Time* magazine pronounced us "one of six of the best" small music festivals in America.

Neighborhood critics responded that few "people around here" like such esoteric music. They suggested alternatives, from mummers' string bands to massed choirs and bagpipers. Indeed, they and others eventually made Mt. Gretna into a veritable live musical iTunes, with a variety of additional "festivals." In 1994, when the old building collapsed like a soufflé under snow and ice, our good fortune increased: The community, enlivened by our success and by the resumed theater productions, built a brand-new and far better replica in fifteen months—one likely to stand for another hundred years.

The main pillar of the success of Gretna Music is the quality of the performances and the music: We didn't compromise on the level of performances or programming just to fill the seats. Over forty-three years, Gretna Music audiences have listened to more than twelve hundred classical and jazz musicians from around the globe, including Grammy winners, MacArthur Fellows, and concertmasters and eminent soloists from several generations of musicians. Some summers we program according to a theme, such as the works of a composer like Schubert or music derived from folk traditions. Chapters 14 and 21 are program notes for two recent summers: Summer of Love in 2016, and summer of Russian Music in 2014, respectively.

Another pillar of our success, the distinctive construction and location of our concert hall, the playhouse, has helped us attract audiences to hear music you wouldn't expect in a forest, except maybe at Tanglewood, Marlboro, or Interlochen. The same music presented in a community building or high school auditorium probably would not have lasted. When it was built, the "Chautauqua Auditorium" was intended for all purposes, including religious services. The celebrated Flonzaley String Quartet once performed there near the turn of the nineteenth-century, and the Chautauqua community staged diverse events, including operettas and concerts. A theater group begun in 1927 continues into the present.

The new playhouse, built to replicate the original as closely as possible, is a perfect size for our music, with about 700 seats. Acoustics are good for an outdoor (and even for an indoor) venue, because the performers and the audience share the same vaulted conical roof, now supported by more substantial posts and enhanced by an acoustical canopy overhead. Air circulates through the three open sides, which allow audience members to gaze around at the century-old cottages while they're hearing unfamiliar contemporary music. An occasional bat buzzing the performers (as violinist Hilary Hahn recalls during her first visit as a child) or a cat parading across the stage serves only to temporarily jolt enchanted listeners back to reality.

Mt. Gretna provides an important ingredient most summer festivals need: a destination aside from the music. Attractions for visitors include the surrounding Gretna community: quaint, distinctive, and a constant source of curiosity and wonder from an earlier century. And there is the Jigger Shop Ice Cream Parlor, Mt. Gretna's most celebrated emblem. But mainly, Mt. Gretna is a place to walk. Or in the words of Thoreau (in his essay "Walking"), "saunter" is explained:

> which word ["sauntering"] is beautifully derived "from idle people who roved about the country, in the Middle Ages, and asked charity, under pretense of going a la Sainte Terre, to the Holy Land. . . .

A Gretna walk will not take you to the Holy Land, or even past many shopping opportunities, but rather past parks, playgrounds, a lake, tennis courts, and most especially through streets and paths lined with all manner of porches, invisible on satellite photos because they are under trees. Many cottages have names like, "U-Needa-Rest" or "Dew Drop In." Walkers may find themselves just feet from occupants, relaxing in old rocking chairs and eager to tell you about (or show you) their cottage and their treasures. One of the old cottages has been turned into a restaurant, where you can have lunch on a porch. Another, next to the playhouse, is home to the Mount Gretna Area Historical Society.

Far from a simple village, Mt. Gretna is really a quilt comprised of fragments of several municipalities—a quilt that gives new meaning to the word "Balkan." Our Balkan Mountains are a few square miles of gentle forested Appalachian foothills and their highest peak, "Governor Dick" hill: elevation, 666 feet. Governor Dick was the last surviving woodcutter, who lived in a lean-to in the Gretna woods. Water runs down Governor Dick into all parts of Mt. Gretna, eventually ending in Lake Conewago. Years of abundant rain and a successful campaign against gypsy moths have brought about the rampant growth of a forest of oak, pine, and poplar trees that, without almost constant pruning and felling, would regularly interrupt power or threaten to engulf entire cottages.

Older Gretna cottages contain wood from chestnut trees from the nineteenth century, largely exterminated throughout the entire U.S. in the early twentieth century by the pathogenic fungus *Cryphonectria parasitica*. My conservation instinct caused me to nurture four chestnut saplings in my yard (which is actually just an extension of the forest) from the fruit of a lone surviving tree that I discovered when some of the acorns I was kicking along a path behind the Campmeeting Tabernacle (a replica of the playhouse, built a year later) turned out to be chestnuts. Maples, invading from the north, expand the fall color palette as the climate warms. The community is further insulated from the outside farmlands by a state game preserve that wraps around much of it.

A neighbor, Fred, called my attention to another possible reason for the attraction of Gretna. Twenty-five years ago, Japanese scientists reported on a small study that suggested that a forest environment could provide humans a lift in mood and relieve stress, and they wondered whether being in a forest might benefit health more than being in a city. Apart from the calming visual images and forest sounds, they postulated that "phytoncides," natural substances released by plants into the environment, might cause salutary effects, such as reduced stress and anxiety, by reducing the stress hormone, cortisol.[265] The Japanese government coined the term *shinrin-yoku*, "forest bathing," to mean that the effect might come from actually breathing in "components emitted from the forest," not simply from escaping the toxicity of urban air. Forests, they theorized, may provide an opportunity to visualize, touch, listen to, and actually inhale nature.

More broadly, *shinrin-yoku* means bathing in biodiversity in an environment more like the one in which humans have evolved for millennia. That theory recalls E.O. Wilson's "biophilia," "the innate pleasure from living abundance and diversity, particularly as manifested by the human impulse to imitate Nature with gardens" and "the innately emotional affiliation of human beings to other living organisms."[266] Scientists usually study humans in "weird" environments—Western, educated, industrialized, rich, democratic, and, mostly, urban—but our species hasn't had the additional hundreds of centuries necessary to evolve into a species well adapted to urban life (and air).[267] "The woods, the trees and the rocks give man the resonance he needs," wrote Beethoven in his only surviving letter to Therese Malfatti (who rejected his marriage proposal, despite his prescient sentiment *and* the gift of his "Für Elise"). Research since then[268] may throw more light on how spending time in forests may relieve various symptoms, possibly improve one's health, and substantiate claims like, "Forest air is the epitome of healthy air…considerably cleaner under the trees, because the trees act as huge air filters…catching large and small particles as they float by"—particles that, per year and square mile, can amount to tons of material.[269] So we might eventually be able to advertise that for the modest price of a concert ticket, you can reinvigorate yourself in a spa of healthy forest bathing—*shinrin-yoku*—while you listen to good music. More fun than pumping iron or jogging! Skeptics can read *two* arguments for this concept.[270]

♫

The only residents who can legally claim to live in Mt. Gretna comprise the approximately two hundred households in the Borough of Mt. Gretna (which also calls itself the "Pennsylvania Chautauqua," and which serves also as a Home Owners Association, and thus has two governing bodies and budgets). Others live in adjacent neighborhoods, all accessible by short walks—called Campmeeting, Mt. Gretna Heights, Conewago Hill, Timber Hills, and Stoberdale—but they actually inhabit the corners of three townships: South Annville, South Londonderry, and West Cornwall, all meeting the borough near the post office. The only remotely common features of the community are the Fire Company, the Sewer Authority, and the Post Office. After twenty-five years I moved uphill into the Heights in Gretna. Now I reside in one ZIP code and receive mail in another!

My short walks to the post office, through the winding tree tunnels that often trap scurrying UPS drivers, take me across two ZIP codes, two townships, three ecclesiastical domains, several school districts, and two electoral districts. Even the county courthouse can be confused with respect to the latter, and my Congressional representative often rejects my gentle suggestions as coming from outside his district, a district that extends all the way to the Philadelphia Main Line. Its shape resembles a pouncing dragon holding my small part of Mt. Gretna in its teeth. (Some Pennsylvania legislators consider that a masterpiece of creativity.) Among the main unifying Gretna ideas is a prevailing conviction that efforts to consolidate services among these quilt patches are actually schemes to increase taxes, though like Californians, most denizens live unaware of the fault lines they cross every day.

As a result of these peculiarities, the actual population of Mt. Gretna is indeterminate: Typical guesses range from sixteen hundred to twenty-two hundred people, the higher figure for summer. And though our forested hills are now surrounded by a sea of cornfields in James Carville's rural "Alabama"* section of Pennsylvania, Mt. Gretna may be an oasis of liberalism owing to a concentration of artists, writers, gay couples, professors, and professionals—if anyone ever cared to ask. There

---

* In a 1986 gubernatorial campaign, James Carville said that politically, Pennsylvania was Paoli (a suburb of Philadelphia—and this morphed *to* "Philadelphia" in subsequent iterations) and Penn Hills (a suburb of Pittsburgh—and this morphed "to "Pittsburgh" in subsequent iterations")—with Alabama in the middle.

is ample representation of the white working class, but as yet little ethnic diversity. The place seems like a small mountain oasis that has emerged like Atlantis from the flat farmlands of Pennsylvania Dutch country.

The most important unifying feature of Mt. Gretna is that people choose to live there because they love it, albeit for varied reasons, and want to participate in community activities. Almost everyone volunteers time and effort, and so each of us has an identification beyond just resident. Many, if not most, join several cultural organizations: the Annual Summer Outdoor Art Show, the Gretna Theater, Gretna Music, the Cicada Festival, Heritage and Bible festivals, Larry McKenna's Mt. Gretna Summer Concerts, the Mount Gretna Area Historical Society, the Annual Tour of Homes, Chautauqua Summer Programs and the Chautauqua Foundation, the Organ Concert Series, the Mt. Gretna Arts Council, Socrates Cafe,* book and film clubs. Some members of each view some of "the others" with suspicion or jealousy, as competitors. And they actually do compete—for contributions, audiences, and venues. A list of Gretna 501(c) organizations would fill a page!

And I should add: There are five restaurants, a country inn, a few small businesses, and, get this, an old indoor roller rink and a Mennonite Psychiatric Hospital! Alas, our narrow-gauge railway, our three hotels, and an amusement park (in a forest, imagine that!) vanished during the last century. We know most of our neighbors and take care of one another, meet often, and pursue many diverse goals. We don't always agree, and discussions sometimes become heated, but when you need help, there is always someone to call.

---

* Socrates Café are gatherings around the world where people from different backgrounds get together and exchange thoughtful ideas and experiences while embracing the central theme of Socratizing; the idea that we learn more when we question and question with others. http://www.philosopher.org/Socrates_Cafe.html

From 2002 to 2013, Bonnaroo was attended by nearly 1 million music fans. Of those million people ten never left the festival. Many applaud Bonnaroo for its relatively low death count.

— Ryan Hogan, "Dying at a Concert Is Easier Than You Think: A Report on Drug-Related Deaths at Concerts"

19

Is There a Doctor in the House?

The tragic onstage collapse and eventual death of oboist Bill Bennett after playing the long, difficult, fifty-seven-bar opening passage of the Strauss *Oboe Concerto* with the San Francisco Symphony came as a shock to everyone. A beloved principal player of that orchestra, and a teacher who aspired to play the oboe the way Ella Fitzgerald sang, he handed his oboe to a violinist—his final conscious act—as he went down. A doctor from the audience jumped onto the stage. Any doctor would have done the same, though the trope "Is there a doctor in the house?" has become just a laugh line for comedians since the advent of "Call 911."

Once evoking John de Lancie's* fateful knock in 1945 on the door of a villa in Garmisch-Partenkirchen at the foot of the Zugspitze Mountain (this story told in chapter 27), the Strauss Concerto from now on will also remind woodwind players and other musicians of the tragic event in Davies Hall. Death from a brain hemorrhage came the next day. Oboists may have second thoughts about climbing that particular musical mountain—needlessly, because an underlying medical cause like an aneurysm, not the concerto, undoubtedly brought down Bill Bennett. For

* John Sherwood de Lancie was an American oboist and arts administrator. He was principal oboist of the Philadelphia Orchestra for twenty-three years and also director of the Curtis Institute of Music.

me, thinking of Bill brings to mind my experiences as a "doctor in the house" in the Gretna Playhouse over more than forty years.

Calmly settling in for a concert one summer evening, I knew what to expect as soon as I noticed the usher walking deliberately into the audience during the opening Haydn String Quartet in F Major, Op. 74, No. 2. He entered from the side, walked purposefully across the front of the hall, then headed up the aisle toward my seat. "Please come with me," he whispered. I followed him as he retraced his steps—all heads in the audience turning, momentarily distracted from the music.

Although there were other physicians in the audience, many of them my friends or acquaintances, I was the one ushers always headed for. As I was the founder of the festival, everyone knew that usually "the doctor is in." Over years of summer concerts, I had come to recognize, and dread, that deliberate, somber approach of an usher.

Three sides of our hall are open to the summer cottages arrayed along the narrow, tree-lined lanes that wind around the back of the theater. Some of those cottages' porches are so close they can serve as box seats—which was the exact intention of their nineteenth-century builders. But sounds travel both ways: Porch conversations as well as motorbikes, barking dogs, and even baby strollers often disrupt the music. The emergency siren is by far the worst distraction, however: It wails three times whenever someone dials 911, each blast seeming interminable during a quiet slow movement. The siren sounded that night as I followed the usher across the adjacent park toward the steps of the one-hundred-year-old wooden Chautauqua Hall of Philosophy—toward, I imagined, the victim.

The audience for classical music is graying, some say—which, theoretically at least, means that concerts of such music are attended by a greater risk of medical events. Some patrons need assistance to transfer into wheelchairs or walkers from cars driven right up to the entrance. Others arrive with even more elaborate medical equipment. Many walk slowly, arm in arm, up the slight incline to the entrance in the back. As I watch them pass by, I wonder who will be next. (Or when will it be me?) They like older classical music—from the eighteenth and nineteenth centuries—especially if it is played by young musicians. And these older generations also prefer jazz by older artists, like the traditional jazz band, The New Black Eagles, that aged thirty-seven years in the course of their annual performances in our concerts.

Fortunately, our classical and jazz performers, including dozens of septua- and octogenarians, have come and gone over the years without incident. I did have to repair Lionel Hampton's vibraphone when a pedal fell off, but I never had to resuscitate Lionel Hampton. Stephane Grappelli ("Hot Club de France") brilliantly made it through his concert at age seventy-seven with the help of most of a bottle of Chivas Regal—stipulated in his contract!—and left the stage unassisted, to raucous cheers and standing applause. Skitch Henderson's onstage stories of working with most of the famous musicians of the past century proved as prodigious as his ability at the piano. Cleo Laine seemed like just another grandmotherly "lady of a certain age" until bathed in stage light and transformed into a lovely, alluring woman with an angelic voice.

I am always amazed by how music, hardwired into the brain during the first decades of life, stays there until the end. Onstage, in their universe, all great performers can seem ageless. The singer Joe Williams ("Every Day I Have the Blues") died at age eighty while walking home from a hospital room that gave him the blues, but not until three years after a warm and lively performance on our stage.

I myself came close to disaster onstage on two occasions. Once, after imbibing at a pre-concert reception—intending to calm my performance anxiety—my blood pressure dropped during a Prokofiev flute sonata to the point where I lost vision for about thirty seconds: I had had an episode of atrial fibrillation, alcohol-induced, that caused orthostatic hypotension. Fortunately I was young and healthy and the rest of my brain continued to function; I remained standing and playing, and vision returned. Another time, after an excessive dose of propranolol (used by some performers to allay stage nerves,) the only casualty was the (Jacques) *Ibert Flute Concerto*. I remained standing but played badly throughout the concerto. (Later, after testing my playing of difficult passages with and without propranolol, I stopped using it, because it did indeed impair my technical ability. There are better methods to deal with performance anxiety—mostly behavioral, not pharmacological.)

As I headed for the Hall of Philosophy on the night in question, memories of earlier urgent summons ran through my head. One August evening, heeding the call, I stepped out from the dimly lit concert hall into total darkness. In my haste to reach a woman outside who had fallen, I forgot about the stone culvert that for more than a hundred years had directed water around the hall rather than into it as it flowed down the side of our modest mountain. My first step was not the nine-inch drop I expected, but four feet to the bottom of the ditch. As my extended right foot finally struck stone, a loud crack accompanied my astonishment. As I continued my fall, my right shoulder struck the side of the culvert. I diagnosed the comminuted fracture of my right humerus before painfully arising, but only after my first step detected the torn Achilles tendon. The fallen woman went home; I went to the hospital.

Another time, an elderly woman fainted in the third row, and the musicians stopped playing. I positioned her flat in the aisle. As she awakened, I learned from her husband that she had "fainted at concerts before." The siren sounded as I helped her walk up the aisle to the back entrance of the hall. The first emergency vehicles arrived, sirens screaming and lights flashing. The rescuers brusquely elbowed me aside, shouting, "Stand back! EMT!" All five vehicles idled (why do they always bring a fire engine?), motors running and lights flashing under the overhanging roof of the hall, as the embarrassed victim, fully recovered and sitting on the steps of the ambulance, completed the necessary insurance forms. Exhaust from the vehicles slowly filled the hall. My request to move them was "interference with a rescue," a charge dismissed only after a thorough, month-long investigation and a warning from the local constable.

I usually have not been able, on these occasions, to summon the wit of a neurologist friend, paged during a concert by the Philadelphia Orchestra: "What time is my appointment tomorrow, doc?"

"You'll have to find another neurologist," he replied, "I just retired." And then Jack retired.

A crowd was gathering in the twilight as I approached tonight's victim. He was a robust, middle-aged man, dressed in shorts and a t-shirt. He appeared dusky and apneic (not breathing), his mouth and already sightless eyes open, a knee brace on his right leg. Again I was asked by an EMT to stand back, this time from a fruitless resuscitation effort. The chest pumping was far too gentle, but I knew he had been asystolic for more than five minutes. One after another screaming and flashing vehicle arrived, their occupants bursting out carrying cases of equipment in both hands. "Anyone know who he is?" they asked. No one responded. I felt helpless, sad, and even a little guilty because I was too late—not participating, not even wanted.

My guilt increased as I deserted the scene and walked back to the theater, and the warm, elegant sounds of the Haydn Quartet, punctuated by still more sirens arriving. After the end of the allegro, I asked the musicians to pause until the sirens stopped. A violinist took the opportunity to talk to the audience, all still oblivious to the drama outside, about the quartet we were playing and why it had begun so loudly and abruptly: It was to command the attention of Haydn's chattering aristocratic audience, he revealed.

Our audience, who had tittered as each siren joined the music, didn't grasp the meaning of the ultimate eerie silence: Rescue efforts had failed, so none of the ambulances raced for the hospital. When the music began again, I couldn't enjoy Haydn's stylish, graceful humor, usually still vital after two hundred years. The Charles Ives quartet was more unsettling to me than the composer intended it to be. The lyrical melodic strains of the final Dvorak quartet, although warm and soothing, didn't fit at all as an impromptu requiem.

The next day's newspaper identified the victim as a mathematics professor at a nearby college, a father of three young children who had just finished his weekly pick-up basketball game. His wife and children had watched the game but were already on the road home when, after visiting the local ice cream parlor with his fellow players, their husband and father collapsed and died.

There was a certain nymph, whose name was
Syrinx who was much beloved by the satyrs
and spirits of the wood . . .
                    — *Bulfinch's Mythology*

20

OLD GOATS PLAYING THE FLUTE

THOUGHTS BEFORE MY PERFORMANCE OF 'SYRINX'

Jupiter disguised his mistress, Io, as a heifer, to hide her from his wife, Juno. Juno saw through the disguise and demanded the heifer as a gift from her husband. Determined to keep Io in her animal state, Juno enlisted Argus, who had a hundred eyes and never went to sleep with more than two eyes at a time, to guard the heifer.

Commanded by Jupiter, Mercury put on his winged slippers and his cap on his head, grabbed his sleep-inducing wand, and leapt down from the heavenly towers to the earth, presenting himself as a shepherd driving his flock. As he strolled, he blew upon his pipes, called the Syrinx or Pandean pipes. Argus listened to the pipes with wonder, having never heard them before. Hoping to lull all hundred eyes to sleep, Mercury played the most soothing strains, and told Argus the story of how the instrument came to be:

> There was a certain nymph, whose name was Syrinx, who
> was much beloved by the satyrs and spirits of the wood; but
> she would have none of them, but was a faithful worshipper
> of Diana, and followed the chase. You would have thought it
> was Diana herself, had you seen her in her hunting dress, only
> that her bow was of horn and Diana's of silver. One day, as she

was returning from the chase, Pan [a demi-god: half man, half goat] approached her. . . . She ran away, without stopping to hear his compliments, and he pursued till she came to the bank of the river, where he overtook her, and she had only time to call for help on her friends the water nymphs. They heard and consented. Pan threw his arms around what he supposed to be the form of the nymph, and found he embraced only a tuft of reeds! As he breathed a sigh, the air sounded through the reeds, and produced a plaintive melody. The god, charmed with the novelty and with the sweetness of the music, said, "Thus, then, at least, you shall be mine." And he took some of the reeds, and placing them together, of unequal lengths, side by side, made an instrument which he called Syrinx, in honour of the nymph.
— from *Bulfinch's Mythology*[271]

Before Mercury had finished the story, he saw Argus's eyes all asleep. As Argus's head nodded forward on his breast, Mercury with one stroke cut his neck through, and tumbled his head down the rocks.

Pan, it might be argued, inspired an entire family of woodwind instruments: The oboe, clarinet, saxophone, and bassoon, as well as their larger and smaller relatives, all produce sound with a vibrating reed. Paradoxically, the flute has no reed; its sound comes from air alone passing over the mouth hole of a reed-like pipe, either across the open end of a pipe closed at the other end or a hole in the side of a pipe near one closed end. Finger holes in effect lengthen or shorten the pipe so you don't need a handful of different pipes—in other words, a real syrinx. The technical simplicity of the flute may explain why it is probably the oldest wind instrument; bone flutes, surviving longer than reed flutes, have been dated by archeologists back to 45,000 BCE.[272]

In French, *flûtiste* means flutist, as does *flautista* in Italian. To answer your next question—one that all flutists are asked: My teacher answered it by saying, "Depends on what the job pays."

Why Debussy wrote "Syrinx" (in 1912) to accompany the death of Pan in the play *Psyche* by Gabriel Mournay is not clear to me. Pan is usually not in the cast of characters of the mythological fable ("Cupid and Psyche") on which the play is based. In performance the flutist remains hidden, as did the musicians who provided dinner music for Psyche's first night in heaven at the magnificent palace before Cupid visited her bed. Perhaps Mournay meant the flutist to be Pan and intended that he died of sorrow at the end of his song.

With its ambiguous harmonies and free rhythm, "Syrinx" sounds like the kind of music Debussy was thinking of when he wrote (writing as "Monsieur Croche" in his column in *La Revue Blanche*, July 1, 1901), "My favourite music is those few notes an Egyptian shepherd plays on his flute: he is part of the landscape around him, and he knows harmonies that aren't in our books." The piece is loaded with whole-tone scales that contain no fifths and no half steps (as discussed in chapter 10), making traditional cadences impossible and eliminating tonic-dominant polarity. Debussy used whole-tone scales often as a way to confound his listeners' tonal expectations and to explore new harmonic possibilities.

Debussy's rhythms also confound. They can be based on length rather than on stress, on long-short rather than strong-weak. Some liken them to the rhythmic principles of French speech, differentiated by syllable length rather than syllable stress.

Syrinx left us not only the family of reed instruments (a class of woodwind blown through reeds and originally made of wood), but also her name: A "syrinx" is the vocal organ of birds; the syringe is a universal medical instrument; and syringomyelia is a condition, inherited or acquired, in which the spinal cord has the shape of a hollow reed. Psyche, meaning both "butterfly" and "soul" in Greek, of course gave her name to the modern disciplines of psychology and psychiatry and their practitioners. Pan lives on in the word "panic." As for old goats like me, they occasionally continue to play flutes.

It has taken far longer for you to read this chapter than the duration of Debussy's "Syrinx" itself (about three minutes). Generations of flutists have played it because it is one of a very few works that a flutist can play alone—and it lends itself to an incalculable number of interpretations.

A fiddler on the roof.
Sounds crazy, no?
But in our little village of Anatevka,
You might say every one of us is a fiddler on the roof,
Trying to scratch out a pleasant,
Simple tune without breaking his neck.
It isn't easy.
You may ask,
Why do we stay up there if it's so dangerous?
We stay because Anatevka is our home.
And how do we keep our balance?
That I can tell you in one word.
Tradition.
— words by Sheldon Harnick, from *Fiddler on the Roof*

21
Russian Festival 2014
A Weird Slice of Music History

M y first experience with Russian music came at the University of Rochester when I helped my roommate, Bob Horick, put on a Russian Arts Festival a few years after the launch of the world's first satellite, the one the Russians called Sputnik (спутник). Among other transformative consequences, the launch caused a spike in enrollment in Russian-language courses, and we both took a few. Our music headliners were the Yale Russian Chorus, a group that imitated the Red Army Choir, undoubtedly penned up in Russia at that time (1960). We also screened Serge Eisenstein's classic 1938 film, Alexander Nevsky, to which Prokofiev contributed a brilliant score that was the first film score that was part of the drama, not just background accompaniment.

A bassoonist then, Bob went on to earn a Ph.D. in Russian—and study, seditiously some may have thought then, at Moscow State University.

As our Russian theme began to materialize for our Gretna Russian Festival in the summer of 2014, curiosity led me to ask Bob (fifty-four years later), "Why is Russian Orthodox church music *a cappella*" (without instrumental accompaniment)? Another Russian scholar, the great Richard Taruskin (who, as I've noted, wrote the entire five-volume *Oxford History of Western Music*), asserts that, in the strict interpretation by the

Orthodox Church, the last verse of Psalm 150—"Let everything that has breath praise the Lord!"—forbids using inanimate musical instruments in worship:[273] That seemed to me strange, because the preceding verses of that psalm (recited to me by my wife, Emi, who never heard of Taruskin) call for praising God with harps, flutes, cymbals, and every other instrument you can think of.*

Bob's answer was: "A single word: tradition," as Tevye sings in *Fiddler on the Roof*. Russian Orthodox writers on music in the church trace back to ancient times the fact that *singing* was how Christians worshipped from the very beginning. In particular, the Russian Orthodox liturgy (primarily the liturgy of St. John Chrysostom) probably traveled from Byzantium via Bulgaria to Russia as singing. In fact, there is nothing *spoken* in it: Everything is chant or *peniye* (pronounced penya) or (*pesnopeniye*): that is, singing or (song-singing). In the words of the musicologist and music critic Joseph Kerman, throughout human history, "heightening by singing has provided words with special emphasis, force, mystery, even magic." (I think Schubert; others may think Billy Joel.)

Bob continued: "When the subject of what we would call music comes up in the Russian Orthodox world, it means "singing." The word for "music" (музыки) is a foreign word in Russian (like the French word "ballet" is in English). Instrumental music has existed in eastern Slavic lands since ancient times, of course, but it was associated with dissolute behavior, especially dancing, drunkenness, and sex. After *old Rus'*** was Christianized in 988, the priests engaged in relentless purging of all native religious beliefs and practices—especially those of the wandering bands of musicians called *skomorokhi (*скоморохъ*).

Skomorokhi were medieval East Slavic harlequins: actors who could also sing, dance, play musical instruments, and compose for

---

* Indeed, the Psalm specifically says, "Praise God (with all these instruments + maybe, with dance)," and concludes, "Let every soul praise God." Musical instruments are forbidden in Orthodox Jewish worship because of specific contingent/subsequent rabbinic enactments—**not** because the Psalm is (or has ever been, so far as I know) interpreted that way.

** Ethnically or ancestrally Scandinavian people trading and raiding on the river-routes between the Baltic and the Black Seas from around the eighth to eleventh centuries.

their oral/musical and dramatic performances. They appeared in Kievan Rus' (principality of Kiev) before the mid-eleventh century, appealing to the common people and usually opposing the ruling groups, the feudal lords, and the clergy, and reached their peak in the fifteenth to seventeenth centuries. They sang mocking songs, staged dramatic and satirical sketches called *glumy* (глумы), and performed in masks and *skomorokhi* dresses to the sounds of string instruments (*domras balalaikas*, *gudoks*), bagpipes, or *bubens* (similar to tambourines). Usually the main character was a fun-loving, saucy *muzhik* (мужик = peasant) of comic simplicity. *Skomorokhi* performed in the streets and city squares, engaging with spectators to draw them into their play. *Skomorokhi* and spectators would sometimes combine their efforts and perform in a *vataga* (big crowd) numbering as many as seventy to one hundred people.

Skomorokhi were persecuted in the years of the Mongol yoke, when the church strenuously propagated ascetic living. A monk chronicler denounced the *skomorokhi* as "devil servants." The Russian Orthodox Church railed against the *skomorokhi* and other elements of popular culture as being irreverent and detracting from the worship of God, or even condemned them as downright diabolical.

In the eighteenth century, *skomorokhi* art gradually died away, passing on some of its traditions in the form of the *balagan* (a scene of chaos or fiasco, as in the opening scene of Stravinsky's *Petrushka*) and *rayok* ("small paradise": a fairground peep show accompanied by lewd rhymed jokes and viewed through a magnifying glass). Shostakovich wrote an "Anti-Formalistic Rayok" cantata mocking Stalin.

"So," continued Bob, "you can see that instrumental music had a very bad reputation among the dominant classes, who were obliged to support the Church's policies." Because of the resistance of the Russian Orthodox church to secular music, Russia was a late starter in developing a native tradition of secular "classical music." (The country, says Taruskin, "emerged as a musical power at about the same point in its history as its emergence as a political and diplomatic power.")[274]

Beginning in the reign of Ivan IV ("The Terrible," 1533–84), the

Imperial Court invited Western composers and musicians to fill this void, and by the time of Peter I ("The Great," 1672–1725), these artists were a regular fixture at Court. While not personally inclined toward music, Peter saw European music as a mark of civilization and a means of Westernizing the country; his establishment of the Western-style city of Saint Petersburg helped foster its spread to the rest of the upper classes. A craze for Italian opera at court during the reigns of Empresses Elizabeth and Catherine also helped spread interest in Western music among the aristocracy. Giovanni Paisiello was among the many long-term musical visitors to Catherine's court. His opera *The Barber of Seville* (based on the play by Beaumarchais)—one of his more than eighty (!) operas—premiered in St. Petersburg in 1782, thirty-four years before Rossini's opera based on the same play.

The first great Russian composer to import native Russian musical traditions into the realm of secular classical music was Mikhail Glinka (1804–57), who composed the early Russian-language operas *A Life for the Tsar* and *Ruslan and Ludmila*. They were neither the first operas in the Russian language nor the first by a Russian, but they gained fame for relying on distinctively Russian tunes and themes, as well as a libretto that employs the vernacular.

Russian folk music became the primary source for the next generation of Russian composers. A group that was inadvertently named by a journalist and called itself "The Mighty Little Band" (*Moguchaya Kuchka*) of talented musical mavericks and autodidacts, headed by Balakirev and including Rimsky-Korsakov, Mussorgsky, Borodin, and César Cui (they were sometimes subsequently referred to by others as "The Five"), proclaimed its purpose to be popularizing Russian national traditions in classical music. They, like Glinka before them, based their works on Russian history, folk tales, and literature, and many are now regarded as masterpieces of romantic nationalism in music. Tchaikovsky was the first Russian composer to rise beyond nationalism and gain international fame, benefiting from the French ballet industry that was then seeking patronage in Russia as its support dwindled in France. He participated in the inaugural concert of Carnegie Hall in 1891.

♫

The lives and works of twentieth-century Russian composers—in particular, Stravinsky, Rachmaninoff, Prokofiev, and Shostakovich—all intersected the World Wars, the 1917 Russian Revolution, and the rise of the Soviet Union. They and others were strongly influenced by these collisions.

Stravinsky found refuge in Paris early enough to escape persecution and to benefit from collaboration with the celebrated dance impresario (and fellow Russian émigré) Serge Diaghilev. He burst onto the world stage at age twenty-eight with three ballets between 1910 in 1913, including *Le Sacre du Printemps*, which caused a riot at its premiere.* The story of that riotous premiere (at least partly planned and ultimately proving to be one of the best marketing strategies in history) is brilliantly told by Thomas Forrest Kelly.[275] Stravinsky later emigrated to New York.

Emigrating on an open sled to Helsinki in 1917 with his family, Rachmaninoff, at age forty-four, also escaped persecution and wars and embarked on a busy career in the U.S. as a pianist and conductor, managed by a concert agent. He became a touring virtuoso pianist, playing his own compositions (like his first, second, and third piano concertos) and living in Hollywood. He carried the burden of feeling, as did others, that he had left his inspiration behind—in Russia and also in the nineteenth century. Two years before emigrating, at the height of his creative powers at age forty-two, he had written his *Vespers* (featured in our Gretna program in 2014), keeping to the church tradition of unaccompanied voices.

There may be a reason you never heard—or heard *of*—Rachmaninoff's *Vespers*. Inna Lobanova-Heasley, a native Russian and a singer with Choral Arts Philadelphia, explained it this way in an onstage conversation before its Gretna performance:

---

* "I think the whole thing has been done by four idiots: First, M. Stravinsky who wrote the music. Second, M. Roerich who designed the scenery and costumes. Third, M. Nijinsky who composed the dances. Fourth, Mr. Diaghilev who wasted money on it." –Enrico Cecchetti, ballet master quoted in "First Nights."

During my first twenty-four years of life in Soviet Russia, having studied classical music and its history at a full-time music school for eight years, I had no idea about the existence of the Vespers or any other sacred music by any . . . composer whatsoever! This is how well this information was locked away from the public eye in the Soviet Union.

I mentioned above how Christianity was brought to Russia almost two millennia ago—its liturgy, primarily by St. John Chrysostom, entirely sung. Though Rachmaninoff avoided affiliation with the established church, he was not an irreligious man, and church music and ritual were powerful influences in his life. His *Vespers* is an English translation of the original *Vsenoshchnoye bdeniye*, literally "All-Night Vigil"—music for a night-long service celebrated in Russian monasteries and, on the eves of holy days, in Russian Orthodox churches. The text contains Russian Orthodox versions of Latin hymns familiar to Westerners, including the "Gloria in Excelsis," "Ave Maria," the "Magnificat," and the "Nunc Dimittis." As in the Latin Vespers service, the source of most of the text is the Book of Psalms and the Gospels. Several sections come from age-old *Znamenny* chants: traditional monophonic songs known from the first consistently identifiable *znamenny* (signs) by which Russian sacred music was notated, the chants dating back at least to the fifteenth century and probably earlier. Others are based on what the Russian church calls Greek chant, a seventeenth-century refinement involving the use of one-note recitatives and simple melismas. Two are traditional Kievan chants, with music alternating, in the style of Ukrainian folk music, between recitative and melodic parts. Finally, two songs are designated as *troparia*—examples of an ancient type of poetic invocation used in Eastern and Russian Orthodox services.

Prokofiev and Shostakovich were virtually prisoners of Joseph Stalin. Lured back from the U.S. to Russia in 1936 (the year he wrote, in Russia, *Peter and the Wolf*), hoping to rescue a faltering career, Prokofiev was largely disappointed—and then the exit doors closed. Unhappy, he left his wife, Lina, for a student, and shortly afterwards Lina was imprisoned for eight years in the gulag. Prokofiev died in 1953 literally unnoticed, because Stalin also died that day and Russians flocked into the streets for days of ceremonies and parades. After her release, Lina spent the rest of her thirty-three years promoting her former husband's reputation and music.

In 1936, after walking out of a command performance of the opera *Lady Macbeth of the Mtsensk District*, Stalin (it is thought; it has never been proved) threatened Shostakovich's life in a "review" he wrote in *Pravda*. The opera was denounced as a "formalistic" work: "a muddle instead of music." The threat could not escape the notice of all Soviet composers, and some sided with the regime. Shostakovich withdrew his *Symphony No. 4 in C minor, Op. 43*—itself a musical prediction of the horrors to come—and offered the seemingly less "formalistic" *Symphony No. 5 in D minor, Op. 47* as "a composer's response to justified criticism." Oblivious to the irony in the subtitle and the "forced rejoicing" in the music, a cheering audience gave him a thirty-minute standing ovation at the premiere in November, 1937. The Fifth may have saved the composer's life (but not the lives of some of his family and friends), and it gave rise to the tendency thereafter to look for hidden messages in Soviet art, and especially in Shostakovich's music.

♫

After World War II, the Soviet Ministry of Culture convened an extraordinary series of conferences between 1946 and 1948 at which charges were brought against deviant artists in literature, film, and music. All were charged with "formalism"—a code word for elite modernism—and with writing works that were "against the people," something that the doctrine of socialist realism expressly forbade (as Aaron Copland was persuaded to tone down the end of his "modernistic" Third Symphony on the U.S. side of the Cold War). Shostakovich's works were banned and he was fired from the Moscow Conservatory, and that is when he wrote his "Anti-Formalistic Rayok" (to the tune of Stalin's favorite song, "Suliko"), satirizing the regime and echoing the medieval *skomorokhi.* Conscripted to write music for Stalin's self-congratulatory films, Shostakovich felt that that assignment may have actually prolonged his life, at least until Stalin died. After the dictator's death, the Fourth Symphony premiered in 1961.

On a rare visit to the West in 1958, according to Isaiah Berlin, "Shostakovich looked like a man who had passed most of his life in some dark forbidding place under the supervision of jailers . . . his face would assume a haunted, even persecuted expression and he would fall into a terrified silence."[276] The humor of his student concerto (*Piano Concerto No. 1, Op. 35a*) eventually turned more dark and sarcastic: Shostakovich was clearly affected by the horror of repression during the war and the Soviet era, and most of his subsequent compositions reflect that. Progressive muscular weakness of his limbs began in 1958 and was never diagnosed by the time of his death in 1975. (It might have been post-polio syndrome because very few individuals with ALS – Lou Gehrig's Disease, another possibility – survive that long.) He continued composing and dedicated his String Quartet No. 8, composed in three days in 1960, "to the victims of fascism and war." His son, Maxim, interprets this as a reference to the victims of all totalitarianism, while his daughter, Galina, says that he originally dedicated it to himself, and that the published dedication was imposed by the Russian authorities. Shostakovich's friend Lev Lebedinsky said that Shostakovich thought of the work as his epitaph, and that he planned to commit suicide around this time.

The death of Stalin brought a liberalizing trend: freedom from musical "accessibility" and "transparency" requirements, and from the sorts of affirmative public statements demanded by the Soviets. Students were no longer expelled from the Moscow Conservatory for possessing Stravinsky and Schoenberg scores, and Soviet musicians came into previously risky and forbidden contact with the music of the European avant-garde typified by (for example) Pierre Boulez. Twelve-tone music began to flourish.

But in the 1970s, Alfred Schnittke abandoned serial technique in favor of an eclecticism that he called "polystylistics."[277] His works, clearly those of a "resentful, marginalized artist," were still prohibited by the Soviet regime until the *glasnost* of Mikhail Gorbachev. Then all hell broke loose, with twenty-two concertos, many composed for an outstanding generation of late-Soviet soloists and abandoning any limits. (Schnittke "undressed in public," one critic said.) His music, wrote Richard Taruskin, contains "plush romantic lyricism, chants and chorales and hymns (real or made up), actual or invented 'historical' flotsam (neoclassic, neobaroque, even neomedieval), and every make and model of jazz and pop" and, Taruskin continues, "tackled life-against-death, love-against-hate, good-against-evil, freedom-against-tyranny, and I-against-the-world," much as Shostakovich had tackled evil-versus-good.

Schnittke began to command Shostakovich's immense following. By the time the Cold War ended in Europe (with the fall of the Berlin Wall in 1989, followed by the dissolution of the Soviet Union in 1991), not only Schnittke but practically his whole generation of Soviet composers, including Sofia Gubaidulina, were living abroad—the result of a mass migration or brain drain that paralleled the one that attended the onset of Soviet power in 1917. Gubaidulina was of actual "Tatar" or Mongolian descent, and her predilection for religious subject matter was considered a mark of political dissidence in the waning years of Soviet authority, which deemed her music "irresponsible." Shostakovich encouraged her to continue down her "mistaken path."

It is always fascinating for me to ponder how the lives of artists affected their work. That is a relatively easy, but frequently sad, task when it comes to Russian composers.

Music is the prism through which I found the code to strangers' inner lives and learned to trust them as neighbours. . . . The truth is that politics, whose currency is power, and economics, whose currency is money, only get us so far. We also need culture, whose currency is trust. . . . It's not enough to outsource culture to the artists and musicians, and receive it as a passive audience. We must engage the full spectrum of human understanding, and every one of us needs to participate in strengthening our cultural resources, all the time—to generate trust and understanding by pursuing basic scientific research, playing music together, or simply looking at the stars.

— Yo-Yo Ma, at the World Economic Forum, Davos, 2017

22
VILLAGE BACH FESTIVAL 1978–98
MUSIC IS BEST AMONG FRIENDS

C ass City, Michigan, has one traffic light. Most of its light changes go unnoticed, but occasionally a red light on Main at the corner of Seeger stops a car or pickup in front of the Eat Shop and Mc-Mahan's Auto Supply on the north, and a pair of pharmacies, inexplicably side-by-side, on the south. On the opposite corners, the Elkland County municipal building and Osentoski Realty complete the two-story center of town. Both Main and Seeger are so wide that a diagonal crossing on foot can be a lonely, windswept expedition.

You get to Cass City from Flint, driving eastward along narrow Route 81 that penetrates flat Michigan militia territory. Caro, midway along the route, feels almost like a last outpost as you leave behind its four traffic lights and Walmart. After fifteen more miles, a grain elevator and the twelve-pump Mini Mart appear on the horizon and then, like twin sentries guarding the entrance to Cass City, McDonald's and Hardee's, on opposite sides of the road. There the two-lane 81 expands into wide Main Street for about four blocks before you reach the lonely traffic light.

If you continue through the light eastward down Main, you pass the traditional red Ben Franklin franchise; then you might see a reporter in the window of the *Cass City Chronicle* typing a story for the next weekly edition. After two blocks you come to the eastern edge of town. Many other storefronts change from year to year; the small business casualty rate is high.

Low clouds shroud Cass City from November to May, thanks to Lake Huron looming to the north—just a short drive beyond the neighboring town of Bad Axe—and also to the east and to the west, where the lake forms Saginaw Bay. Locals call this broad peninsula the "thumb" of Michigan. Its bleak, logged landscape yields mostly beets—truckloads of them parade out for months every fall—and contrasts with the stately pines and blue lakes of the Grand Traverse and the Upper Peninsulas to the northwest, summer playgrounds of urbanites from points south. Cass City's only motel closed about nine years ago.

Once a year, at Thanksgiving, Cass City becomes the unlikely site of a musical experience probably as moving and memorable as any in eighteenth-century Leipzig, when Bach was Kantor at St. Thomaskirche. (Or so we would like to think. Actually, Bach's congregation arrived late, gossiped, strutted about, and flaunted their social standing during the Sunday premieres of most Bach cantatas.[278]) For two decades, musicians from all over the country have come with their families to play together at the Village Bach Festival. Throughout the four-day Thanksgiving weekend, the First Presbyterian Church at the corner of Church and Seeger streets, one block north of the traffic light, resonates with music. The small community provides and listens.

On Thanksgiving afternoon, musicians arrive from as far as Iowa, North Carolina, and New York and head for the home of Lambert and Holly Althaver, founders of the festival, who continue to lovingly nurture it. Inside the Althavers' ever-open front door, they find old friends already relaxing in the warm parlor, redolent of roasting turkey. This large, book-lined room, built onto their modest two-story home for just this purpose, easily accommodates about thirty musicians and their families and friends, the omnipresent TV football muted and barely noticed. For some, this annual renewal of friendships and reunion of families took place for the entire twenty years of the festival. These veterans have seen several of their children grow into professional musicians and take seats beside them in orchestras, including those in Cleveland and Chicago.

After initial acquainting and reacquainting, a glass of wine, hors d'œuvres, and a traditional Thanksgiving dinner, singers of arias and their basso continuos walk two blocks through light snow to the church for the first rehearsal. Dessert is delayed until their return two hours later. At some point, Holly and Bert's neighbors arrive to escort each visiting family to their homes, where they will reside for the next three days of rehearsals and concerts.

Rehearsals occupy most of the musicians until the last of three performances on Sunday afternoon. All day Friday and Saturday, Music Director Don Jaeger, his conducting style low-key but efficient, rehearses the small chamber orchestra and four singers, who also serve occasionally as a chorus (perfectly adequate in size for such a small place, especially since they have also sung with Robert Shaw.) Most chamber works, sonatas, and solos have been prepared earlier and are informally polished during rehearsal breaks in the basement of the church. Listening to rehearsals is the highlight of the weekend for many of the family members, musician hosts, and community residents, who provide an attentive audience all day.

At about 11 o'clock each morning a tantalizing aroma begins to permeate the rehearsal—emanating from the church basement, where the Presbyterian women prepare lunch. Each member of the church's volunteer cooking staff proudly contributes a different favorite dish each day and helps prepare mid-morning and afternoon snacks. The Althavers supply lavish pre- and post-concert dinners on Friday and Saturday, and the Masonic Lodge serves brunch on Sunday.

Each year the festival opens and closes with a major work of Bach—a "Bach Sandwich," as it were—but in between is a range of music from the past three centuries, last year ranging from John Dowland's "Flow My Tears" to Samuel Barber's "Dover Beach" and including a premiere of Allen Krantz's *Summer Music* for flute and guitar, performed by the composer and yours truly. Audiences of earlier years have heard a substantial number of Bach's 180 cantatas, Mozart's *Exultate Jubilate* and *Duo Concertante,* Bach's *Brandenburg*, violin, oboe d'amore, and harpsichord concertos, *Morgen* as well as horn and oboe concertos by Richard

Strauss, *To Be Sung upon the Water* by Domenick Argento and *Cuato Madrigales Amatorios* by Joachin Rodrigo, Mozart and Tchaikovsky serenades for strings and more, the "Adagietto" from Mahler's *Fifth Symphony*—an incredible variety of repertoire. (Concertmaster Bill Preucil had performed the entire Mahler Fifth the night before in Cleveland, also as concertmaster. "I hope you will do better," he quipped to Maestro Jaeger.)

When the builders replaced the original wooden First Presbyterian Church in 1906 with the present American Gothic structure, they installed a dozen beautiful stained glass windows: They still illuminate a small sanctuary that seats no more than two hundred souls in gently curving diagonal rows facing the pastor's lectern in the left front corner. This arrangement leaves a cramped triangular space for a small orchestra in front of the first row of pews, but requires the harpsichord, singers, and soloists to locate behind it on a narrow elevated stage directly in front of the Henry Erben organ, set squarely in an alcove in the front wall of the sanctuary. The need to either retire or rehabilitate the instrument in 1976 catalyzed the Bach Festival—and the restored organ still lends its image to festival programs and brochures.

The parishioners are proud of their organ, built in 1865 in Flint and moved decades later to Cass City. It is a self-contained instrument: Its "tracker" mechanism, console, and 305 speaking and ornamental pipes all fit into a black walnut case barely larger than a nineteenth-century French armoire, which it closely resembles. To the consternation of visiting organists, the spacing of the foot pedals is arbitrary. Built to be inexpensive and mobile, it makes up in charm for what it lacks in versatility and stamina. With a pitch somewhat indefinitely between early and modern, it is mainly suited for accompanying the congregation. Even so, and despite valiant efforts by Layton James, keyboardist of the St. Paul Chamber Orchestra, the soft-spoken gentle beast gave up last year halfway through "For the Beauty of the Earth,"* probably exhausted by having to produce so many notes in so short a time.

The Village Bach Festival owes its special character to a felicitous combination of talents among its founders, Don Jaeger and Lambert

* A Christian hymn by Folliott S. Pierpoint

and Holly Althaver. Jaeger, founder of several other festivals—most are now only history after short but illustrious lives—relies on hundreds of friends he made over forty years as an oboist, teacher, arts administrator, fund-raiser, and conductor. Many of the musicians in Cass City have been regulars in "Jaeger" orchestras in Michigan, Texas, and California or at his festivals in other states and overseas, or at still other festivals where he has been an invited oboist or conductor, including Music at Gretna in Pennsylvania. Still others have been Jaeger's students at the Interlochen Arts Academy, where he was director as well as oboe teacher.

So one of Jaeger's talents has, obviously, been the lifelong building and maintenance of a network of musical friends. With little effort, he can field any group, from a quintet to an orchestra, that can sound like a seasoned ensemble after one rehearsal. You may find Cleveland Orchestra concertmaster Bill Preucil, both of his parents, and many others from the extended Preucil family in the string sections, Elaine Douvas from the Metropolitan Opera Orchestra as oboist, or Penelope Jensen singing a cantata that she recorded with Robert Shaw. Jaeger never forgets a good musician, and always looks for opportunities to make music. His longtime friend and assistant, violinist Julia Kurtyka, adds humor as she makes sure musicians are in their chairs on time and that music is on the stands.

Lambert Althaver joined Walbro Corporation in Cass City in 1954 as an accountant just out of Principia College, then married Holly, the daughter of the company's founder. Neither planned to spend their lives in Cass City, but that became virtually inevitable when Lambert became CEO of the company. To make a long story short, the Village Bach Festival is one way they both adapted to that eventuality. (Ironically, the $25,000 that local merchants invested in 1954 to attract Walbro to Cass City has grown into millions, enabling many of them to escape to a warm retirement.)

Walbro makes small engine carburetors, in Cass City and also in Japan, Mexico, and Singapore. The immaculate interior of the recently the modernized plant—a world of its own in the middle of town—hums with dozens of robots turning out small precision parts destined for the insides of small engines that power lawnmowers, chainsaws, and automobiles, including most made by Chrysler and many by Ford. Lambert's costly success in fending off a hostile takeover in 1988 was the subject of an article in *Forbes*, "Invasion of the Company Snatchers." Lambert applies his corporate management skills to the festival to ensure that tickets are sold, and musicians are retrieved at the Detroit airport and paid at the end of the festival.

Holly, a lover of music and veteran promoter of the arts in Michigan, inspired the festival, and continues largely responsible for the warm and well-organized hospitality, offered in this case by the Cass City community, that is essential to the success and survival of any festival of this kind. She shares with Lambert the annual burden of raising the necessary contributions to cover the costs not met by ticket sales.

As a musician, to be paid for travel and performance while you are pampered and fed during four days of pure pleasure adds to the feeling that the experience is an annually recurring dream. In a modern America increasingly indifferent to the art to which many classical musicians have dedicated their lives, here is a small, obscure oasis where the honest, intimate, and unamplified expression of music at its finest is still valued.

Signs of change, however, were not hard to detect. Each year volunteers and hosts were more difficult to find, as family ties and other pursuits took them to distant locations, a problem that increased the burden on the Althavers. Without their guiding presence, the festival would have long since ceased to exist, and both were nearing retirement; other members of the Walbro founding family have departed for more favorable climes, where Bach festivals are far from anyone's mind. The empty seats at some performances, although small in number, always remind us that most people prefer holiday football to Bach cantatas.

Addendum, 2018: The festival finally closed in 1998, after twenty years. Lambert retired, and the Walbro Company moved its operations to Mexico. Cass City fell upon even harder times. But residents of the small lakeside city of Lexington, forty-five minutes away, imported the entire festival—Jaeger and all the musicians—to their town, where it celebrated its nineteenth anniversary in 2018.

"The Broken Chord"
— *The New York Times*, December 11, 2005

23
THE AUDUBON STRING QUARTET
WHEN A COURT SILENCED MUSIC

laying in a string quartet is not for faint-hearted conservatory graduates. Contrary to what the public might assume, success takes far more than two violinists, a violist, and a cellist with chairs and music stands getting together for concerts. When you graduate from a conservatory and join three others, you face an uncertain future of stiff competition for recognition and employment in a culture that may seem increasingly uninterested in your music. Your assets might include only your instrument, your skill, a few friends in the music world, and, hopefully, an apartment large enough to seat four. All that after sacrificing a normal teenage life for many hours of instrumental practice. The only survivors are those with a deep passion for the medium, high proficiency, a tolerance for an itinerant life (often in the back seat of an SUV, or next to your belted cello in coach class), and the temperament to work and live intimately with others. Plus a decent share of lucky breaks.

A young quartet faces years of daily rehearsals with no guarantee that anyone will ever hear the results. The chances of getting good enough to win a competition, attract a manager, and embark on a career together remain small even if all four members rehearse every day for months, or years. If one member takes a paying job to cover the rent, that limits rehearsal time. If a member drops out to attend veterinary school or proves to be incompatible, musically or personally, the others, after searching for and auditioning a replacement, must start again almost from the beginning. And as with all freelancing, you leave behind the security of a regular salary and benefits from an employer, not to mention the regular audience enjoyed by an orchestra musician. Oh, and multiply the divorce rate by four and you get the approximate risk.

As a consolation, you have the regular collegiality of three other humans and some strength in numbers, as each member may contribute a different non-musical skill, like managing the small payroll or driving the van. That is a better life, perhaps, than that of your pianist friends who spend most of their time with a large immobile instrument that cares nothing about their fears or dreams. Plus you have the freedom to, with your fellow musicians, devise your own repertoire and schedule rather than have to submit to the whims of conductors and the requirement to play any music that someone sets on your music stand.

It is a fortunate quartet that retains the same members for more than a few years, much less for more than a generation. In *Indivisible by Four,* violinist Arnold Steinhardt describes the tricks required to keep all four members of the Guarneri Quartet together for forty-five years, including dining at separate tables at the same restaurant and traveling by different routes to the same tour stops. Over the years, each member learns to adapt in many ways.

One difficulty in string-quartet intonation is to determine the degree of freedom you have at any given moment. Two factors come into play: the linear and the vertical. By "linear" I'm referring to the sense of melodic or harmonic direction in the individual line; semitones in particular have a tendency to be drawn slightly up or down as the case may be. In this sense, "expressive intonation" is an essential element of interpretation. The other factor—the vertical—is the necessity to be in tune with your colleagues, to hear your individual note in relation to the chord being played at that moment. Both factors are important and demand a highly responsive ear and instant adaptability ... the linear and vertical demands sometimes conflict. [279]

The interaction among quartet members in a practice room might amaze any casual observer (or intrepid psychologist) on at least two levels: musical and human. On the musical level, there is an endless give-and-take. "I would play that G-flat slightly higher, because the viola has the subdominant note between the cello and the second violin in that chord, while the first violin plays the tonic and then moves to ...," or "You are always a little late in that entrance," or "Can you make that sound a bit more threatening?" The total of all these micro-negotiations determines the character (and often the success) of the next performance, but the results are not set forever, because the concept of any work evolves over the lifetime of the ensemble, changing over time and even from concert to concert, though the name of the piece on the program remains the same. The countless interpretations of a Beethoven quartet, or of any classical work, keep the music living; there is no correct or perfect way to play any of them. New sounds and insights are always in the score, waiting to be discovered. The ultimate goal is to play music as if four players were actually one, with a coherent concept of the piece through which they can connect to the lives and hearts of their listeners, regardless of their continent of residence or their native language.

The second, non-musical level is a micro-model or petri dish for human society at large. Constant give-and-take musical exchanges require all members to respect the playing and views of the others, to listen to them, and to have both the skill and the tact to criticize while being open and receptive to criticism—qualities notably rare in much current discourse in our general culture. They become second nature, however, to the best small-ensemble musicians. Cliques (and intramarriages), hierarchy, and segmentation into leaders and followers can lead to conflict and instability. Insults, grudges, innuendo, and *ad hominem* arguments have no place. No wonder many musicians choose to audition for a symphony orchestra, accept a teaching job, or settle into an orchestra pit and hundreds of numbing performances of *The Lion King*. Clearly, dedication—to the music and to the life—self-selects members of most successful string quartets. When musical and interpersonal compatibility breaks down, the music—and the life of a string quartet—suffers. The thirty-seven-year life of the Audubon Quartet was illustrative—as well as, in its day, illustrious.

Clyde (Tom) Shaw, the cellist, founded the quartet in 1974 when the original members had some "Audubon" connection, such as Audubon Park, where violinist Janet, then a member of the New Orleans Symphony, went to wax her car. Tom had a girlfriend who lived in an Audubon Park in Florida. Although Doris Lederer, the violist, had no Audubon association (as namesake naturalist John James Audubon had none with music), she joined in 1976 after graduating from the Curtis Institute of Music. Eventually, having worked and traveled together for twelve years, Tom and Doris succumbed to the almost inevitable: Both left their spouses and married in 1988, and also remained married to the quartet until it came to the end of its natural life in 2011. The name Audubon, regardless of its lack of allusion to any aspect of music, proved attractive and enduring. Maybe the suggestion of songbirds helped.

The original association between Music at Gretna, the summer festival I began in 1976, and the Audubon resulted from a mixture of good fortune and serendipity. It is accurate to say that Music at Gretna would not have succeeded without the Audubon. After our first year, it was obvious that we needed an accomplished professional ensemble willing to work with other musicians, bring musician friends to the festival, and play their own repertoire, seasoned by years of rehearsal and performance. Otherwise, rehearsals for our concerts, with strangers coming together for the first time, would take too much time and produce less good music.

By a stroke of good fortune, the Audubon lived less than two hours away, in residence at Marywood College in Scranton, and were searching for a place to spend their summers after winning three international competitions. A mutual friend, Dr. Tim Carter, contrabassist and my colleague at the Penn State Medical Center in Hershey, made the connection. By a twist of fate, the trip from Marywood to Mt. Gretna takes one right past John James Audubon's first home in America, in Mill Grove, Pennsylvania, whose Audubon Center preserves his legacy.

During our first decade, the Audubon appeared in most of our concerts, not only as a string quartet but as the core of other ensembles: trios, piano quintets, sextets, octets, and even as a small "orchestra" for our tenth-anniversary performance of all six Brandenburg Concertos. They indeed brought friends as well as made friends here, and invited them to play in their concerts elsewhere during the year. They also endeared themselves to the denizens of Mt. Gretna—so much so, in fact, that dinner invitations had to be scheduled far in advance. (The quartet themselves hosted as many dinners as anyone else!) One summer the quartet had to leave Mt. Gretna on twenty-four-hour notice to perform at the White House at the invitation of President Carter. The Audubon was the first Western ensemble to play and teach in China, presaging and helping to start a surge of interest in Western classical music among students in southeast Asia, who have since flooded the leading American conservatories and concert stages.

As years passed, housing in Mt. Gretna became more expensive, as summer guests occupied cottages formerly available for musicians. As victims of our own success, we were almost priced out of the rental market! Nevertheless, only one summer passed without an Audubon visit to Mt. Gretna. That was when they were invited to Brazil. In a stroke of infelicitous timing, that summer (1980), *Time* magazine included Music at Gretna in a story, "Six of the Best Small Music Festivals in the US"— that accolade ironically resulting in large part from the Audubon's presence in previous festivals. And it was then that the ten-year tradition of an Audubon summer-long residency at Gretna began to change, as our programming diversified and their availability became limited as a result of invitations from other summer festivals: Chautauqua, New York; Blue Hill, Maine; Newport, Rhode Island; and Idyllwild, California.

And there was the violin problem. Dennis Cleveland was the first violinist when the Audubon first came to Gretna in 1977, and also when they won the competitions that launched their career. Though he was a fine violinist, Dennis was difficult for the others to work with, and sometimes late or absent for rehearsals. I remember him mostly for his remark on arriving for a rehearsal of the Schubert Octet with three principal wind players of the Chicago Symphony: "I hope you orchestra players know how to play chamber music!" Perhaps not fully appreciating the irony, he departed shortly afterwards, not happily, for the Metropolitan Opera Orchestra as the Audubon began their long residency at Virginia Tech in 1981. (A residency at a conservatory or university is coveted by any freelance ensemble, because it provides a home base and a regular, though usually small, salary.)

After four temporary violinists over several years, the next permanent first violinist again began to prove that without compatibility, both musical and personal, making good music together can be challenging. David Ehrlich's tenure brought fourteen years of increasing conflict that was too often reflected in the music. There was acrimony in the rehearsal room and on many tours, related in part to a difference regarding the concept of a string quartet: Is it a collaboration of four equal players, or a violin soloist accompanied by three others? (As would be the case in most string quartets, three members of the Audubon strongly advocated the former.) David's eventual long-overdue separation from the quartet finally ended dissension and was triggered by a commitment made by him, unknown to the three other members, for the quartet to play free concerts for anyone contributing toward his purchase of a valuable old Italian violin. Another dispute concerned which violinist would play when the Audubon performed string trios. After he threatened to argue these and other issues through his lawyer, one day David found a letter from another lawyer on his music stand: the dreaded "pink slip" from the other members of the Audubon.

A flurry of legal actions led to an unprecedented restraining order against public performances by the remaining three members. The Audubon may be the only ensemble in history to risk imprisonment by playing music, as they courageously did with or without various substitute first violinists more than once on the Gretna stage. (Their courage didn't help me avoid a $2 million lawsuit for hiring them—ultimately, but not inexpensively, dismissed.) Eventually, a corporate law judge, obviously ruling on his first case involving an incorporated string quartet, awarded the terminated violinist a quarter of the quartet's "value" based on his estimate of future earnings. That settlement was accompanied by fees from seventeen lawyers totaling far more than $1 million, and it totally depleted the assets of all four members.

After multiple appeals, the grand finale of the legal imbroglio in 2008 attracted worldwide attention and sympathy: A court order required Tom, Doris, and their new second violinist to relinquish their instruments, along with their cars, homes, snow blowers, and other assets, in order to pay the judgment. A group of "angels," including supporters of Gretna Music, assisted in the repurchase of some of the instruments from a sympathetic instrument dealer who had acquired them so that they could be leased back and eventually repurchased.

The Audubon emerged from an eight-year ordeal in 2008 sounding more like their original, prize-winning self, with a new, more compatible first violinist who amicably alternated between violin chairs during the quartet's final years; but undoubtedly a serious toll was taken on the health of all involved. In 2011 the Audubon finally stopped performing as a quartet, though each member has continued their career as freelance musicians and teachers.

"It is a bitter story," wrote Daniel J. Wakin in his December 11, 2005, story "The Broken Chord" about the quartet in the *New York Times*, "in which music plays no redemptive role."

I appreciate your offer of a kitten . . . I had been eyeing as a possible pet a rather pleasant-looking green snake named Freddy, but accidentally ran over him with the power mower last Monday. And I can't work up much enthusiasm for the two rabbits in the yard, since I suspect that they are the ones who have been getting into the basil.

— Jerry Bramblett, during his first semester as Professor of Statistics at the University of Connecticut

24

A (Funny) Polymath

Gretna audience members of a certain age may remember a pianist named Jerry Bramblett, who played during the first ten years of Gretna Music. I met Jerry at the Interlochen Center for the Arts (then called "National Music Camp") in 1956, because in high school he was a flutist as well as a pianist, a year older than I. We competed against each other in weekly "tryouts and challenges" for top seats in the orchestra. In his last year, he won the concerto competition playing the new flute concerto by Jacques Ibert. A year later I won playing the same piece, because he coached me and accompanied me at the audition. (He had prepared for his own audition by playing with a piano accompaniment he had recorded himself.)

Jerry left Yale just as I arrived there for medical school. He went to Columbia to get a Ph.D., but mainly to study the piano—in secret, because his scholarship was to study statistics. We played flute and piano music every third weekend in his aunt's studio apartment over the Cliffmore Bar on Second Avenue in Manhattan, dined at a restaurant recommended in *New York on $5 a Day*, and then usually repaired to an off-Broadway play.

Some would call Jerry a polymath as he excelled in a variety of pursuits: actually just about anything he put his mind to, including languages, mathematics and statistics, cooking—his fusion of his mother's

Southern style and French cuisine—and music. Anything that didn't demand much physical coordination. Even not remotely delicate objects broke in his hands, not to mention countless wine glasses. By just walking past an end table he could cause a lamp to crash to the floor. Once, as we pulled out of the driveway en route to a ten-day vacation, he jumped out and ran back into the house for a last-minute pit stop. Flipping up the toilet seat, he didn't notice that his vigorous effort had cracked the tank. On our return, the basement of our rented house contained as much water as the entire Kirkwood Missouri water supply. Alas, Jerry's clumsiness was reflected, albeit subtly, in his piano technique—obviously a serious limitation. Amateur psychologists of his day probably called him a "left-brained" person. But pianists need both sides of the brain!

Between my visits to New York, we corresponded. I still read his letters.

About his Russian class at Columbia:

Ah, the delights of fluency in the foreign tongues! I now have six cases at my disposal and thirty or so exciting verbs to boot. I am still bothered a bit about the niceties of the language, as when, the other day, I missed the endings of four consecutive adjectives and left poor Mrs. Berryman in tears, but am trying to develop an ambiguous grunt which will pass for any ending. My efforts at the blackboard are thoroughly professional, however, and I am beginning to receive threatening notes from the less gifted members of the class. I am worried about Mrs. Berryman; she is ill nowadays. Yesterday, as I was struggling erroneously through "That fine summer day I took a walk in the woods with my beloved dog," she got dizzy and had to sit down.

About his apartment on West End Avenue in Manhattan, in a prewar building with large rooms:

I am sitting on the floor of my new pad. The kitchen alone sleeps four.

About a visit to his apartment by a former professor at Yale:

We brought the festivities to a close the next morning with breakfast and a reading (complete) of the Handel flute sonatas. The latter was a trifle bizarre, insofar as the harpsichord had not been tuned for two weeks, Janet had never been exposed to the treacheries of said instrument, and I had not touched the flute since Interlochen, but it was fun, and I noticed afterwards that I had no hangover and have not made any errors in prepositional case endings since.

About a visit to a friend:

We stopped by the medical school to visit a friend of David's who is in the psychiatric institute there. A tragic, but rather romantic case: the son of one of David's teachers at Harvard Med School who flunked out of Harvard his freshman year and promptly went mad. I explained probability theory to him.

Offering advice about my girlfriend, who had spoken of entering a convent:

As for her convent-ional leanings, I think a well fashioned julep (made from the small, darker leaves) to be the handiest and most pleasant of dissuaders.

Anticipating fine food and wine and a visit to New Haven:

I must away and prepare a sauce duxelles aux champignons for supper. If it is any good, I will put some in an envelope and send it to you. It is essential that the champagne be cold, and I recoil at the embarrassment and risk of nursing decanters of chilled spirits aboard the New Haven coaches.

Requesting a medical consultation from me, a first-year medical student:

When you get a chance, please send me the musical remedies for the following: (1) blister on palm from hanging curtains, (2) sunburn on left shoulder blade from asymmetric exposure, (3) small pimple under navel, source unknown, (4) hangover, from next Sunday's picnic.

Regarding the first month of his job:

My first real challenge as a professor of Statistics comes this Sunday, when I shall play host to the statisticians barbecue and beer-blast. Fortunately, this will require no greater efforts than preparing the fields for softball and volleyball, and gathering a few tomatoes and apples, in which activities I will have the assistance of David, who is coming up for the weekend, so I will be able to establish myself as the perfect host. How well I shall do the next morning at my first lecture I shall not venture to guess.

Reviewing his own concert:

No doubt I played badly, but I think, with occasional inspiration. The audience was large and vapid, but happily sprinkled with wine beforehand and during and kept its distance, more or less.

About his piano:

I especially envy your perfectly tempered Steinway. Mine, alas, as a result of a recent tuning by Rockville, Conn.'s most distinguished tuner, a complete nut, has developed a rather evil temper, refusing to enter the keys of A-flat and E major, to which I occasionally have recourse.

On pets:

I appreciate your offer of a kitten, but my enthusiasm for animal companionship has dimmed somewhat since I kept a colleague's part-beagle for a few days while he was at a convention. The beast was advertised to be newspaper trained but sadly did not seem able to distinguish between the New York Times *and a scatter rug, much less between a Steinway leg and a fireplug. I was a wreck before the week was out. Recently I had been eyeing as a possible pet a rather pleasant-looking green snake named Freddy, but accidentally ran over him with the power mower last Monday. And I can't work up much enthusiasm for the two rabbits in the yard, since I suspect that they are the ones who have been getting into the basil.*

Jerry passed away in 1995, leaving a small delegation of devoted friends, as well as piano students who had studied with him at Mansfield University and the University of Wisconsin. (He had remained a statistics professor at the University of Connecticut for only three years—while he got a degree in music.) If you find similarities in these excerpts to my own writing, now you'll know why.

Music is the favorite passion of my soul and fortune has cast my lot in a country where it is in a state of deplorable barbarism.
— Thomas Jefferson, from *Jefferson Himself*,
edited by Bernard Mayo

25
THOMAS JEFFERSON & MUSIC

Reading Jon Meacham's marvelous *Thomas Jefferson: The Art of Power*,[280] I noted references to Jefferson's love of music, and found my way back to *Thomas Jefferson and Music* by Helen Cripe[281] and then to *Jefferson Himself*, a volume entirely of Jefferson's own words, edited by Bernard Mayo,[282] to expand on the subject.

Jefferson indeed loved music, and especially enjoyed playing the violin and singing with his sister Jane when he was young. Later he encouraged his family to play and study music as part of his quest to provide them with a broad education like his own (and to develop what he called "resources against ennui"). He wrote his daughter Patsy: "With respect to the distribution of your time, the following is what I should approve: From 8 to 10, practice music . . ."[283]

Jefferson acquired several violins, all lost now, in addition to harpsichords and pianos and a glass armonica, a bizarre instrument using glasses filled with water, invented by Benjamin Franklin. (Mozart wrote a quintet for it.*) It isn't clear that Jefferson understood that studying and playing music can have the strong impact on the brain and on learning in general that we know about now, but he did realize

---

* "Adagio and Rondo for Flute, Oboe, Viola, Cello and Glass Armonica in c minor, K. 617" - 1791

that playing and appreciating music, like enjoying the other arts, could enrich one's life. The Jefferson family's large collection of music, the Monticello Music Collection stored in the Alderman Library in Charlottesville, ranges far and wide in style and origin.

Visitors hosted by Jefferson at his home at Monticello remarked about the wonderful evenings with good food and wine, sophisticated conversation, and musical performances, usually including those by Jefferson himself. One wonders how good a violinist he was. Contemporaries extolled his musicality, likely for their own various purposes. The most reliable critic was probably granddaughter Ellen Wayles Randolph Coolidge:

With regard to Mr. Jefferson's skill on the violin . . . Mr. Randall's idea that he became "one of the best violinists of his day" is a little extreme. My grandfather would, I believe, have disclaimed it. When we remember that the violin is a most difficult instrument, and that great proficiency in the management of it requires the labor of a life—that sixteen hours out of twenty-four have sometimes been devoted to it, we see at once that the time given to music by Mr. Jefferson could never have accomplished more than a gentlemanly proficiency. No amateur violinist could hope to equal a professor. Mr. Jefferson played I believe very well indeed, but not so well as to stand a comparison with many other persons especially such as he must have met with abroad. [284]

Jefferson must have heard a lot of good music in Paris; Mozart's opera *The Marriage of Figaro* premiered during his five years there. Regarding music in Paris, he wrote that music "particularly is an enjoyment the deprivation of which with us cannot be calculated. I am almost ready to say it is the only thing which from my heart I envy them [Parisians]." And in the rhapsodizing we quoted above, "Music is the favorite passion of my soul," he contrasts the "state of deplorable barbarism," which he deplored in his own country, with the state of music in another European country:

In a country like [Italy], music is cultivated and practiced by every class of men I suppose there might be found persons of these trades who could perform on the French horn, clarinet, or hautboy, and bassoon, so that one might have a band [at Monticello, perhaps]. . . Sobriety and good nature would be desirable parts of their characters.[285]

Sobriety and good nature, of course, being well-known traits of musicians.

Some observers have suggested, though, that "a state of deplorable barbarism" was a little too extreme a characterization of American music in Jefferson's lifetime. (Others wonder whether he listened to the music his 600 slaves might have made.) But consider the following announcement of an event in Williamsburg—when Jefferson was probably in town—from *Thomas Jefferson and Music*. It calls to mind some suggestions for what Gretna Music could present in place of arcane chamber music to build our audience.

By Permission of his excellency, the governor, for the entertainment of the curious:

On Friday the 14th of this Instant April [1769] will be exhibited, at the theater in Williamsburg, by Peter Gardiner, a curious set of figures, richly dressed, four feet high, which shall appear upon the stage as if alive; to which will be added a tragedy called Babes in the Wood; also a curious view of waterworks, representing the sea, with all manner of sea monsters sporting upon the waves. Likewise fireworks, together with the taking of the Havannah, with ships, forts, and batteries, continually firing, until victory crowns the conquest; to which will be added a curious field of battle, containing the Dutch, French, Prussian, and English forces, which shall regularly march and perform the different exercises to great perfection.

The performer will lay his head on one chair and his feet on another, and suffer a large rock of 300 weight to be broke on his breast with a sledge hammer. Tickets to be had at the Raleigh Tavern. . . . "[286]

…the owner led them into a large salon with a piano and served tea and cakes…

26

HE COMMANDEERED A VILLA
—BUT NOT JUST ANY VILLA

We just learned that a former neighbor in Mt. Gretna, Ted Kramers, passed away last week. Ted was well into his nineties and still vigorous. He told me the following story about ten years ago. It's the same story that Alex Ross relates in *The Rest Is Noise* (in the chapter "Zero Hour: The US Army and German Music, 1945–1949"), where Ted is called "John" Kramers and Sgt. Greiss is called Lt. Weiss.[287] Other differences in our two accounts may relate partly to Ted's memory: He was in his late eighties when I spent several hours with him to record the details. (My memory is no better than his, but I took notes. He was John Theodore Kramers.)

In April 1945, Ted, a major in a Civil Affairs unit, entered Germany with the 103rd Division of the U.S. Army. The division moved east toward Munich and then turned south toward Garmisch, Innsbruck, and the Brenner Pass, to link up with other American forces moving north from Italy. They felt safe, he said, and "loose," because they realized that the Germans were on the run and the end of the war was near. But they were aware that they might stumble upon a "redoubt" where loyal units of the SS or Wehrmacht might make a last stand in the remote southern corner of Germany. Ted also remembers feeling then, as he said most American soldiers did, that the German army usually "played by the rules," and so he planned to be careful to "handle things correctly" as he dealt with the formalities of ending the war. Meyer Levin, in the *Saturday Evening Post*, described Ted as "a spirited fellow who whistled through a youthful blond moustache." Ted's wife, Ellen, confirmed that when I visited them. His moustache by then white, Ted "wanted to move at the head of the pack" on their many tourist excursions all over the world, she said.

Ted and his driver, Sgt. Greiss, went ahead of the division to locate a place for their next headquarters in Garmisch. En route they encountered survivors fleeing from Dachau, and also were ordered to accept the surrender of a small unit of Hungarians—who rewarded them with a huge supply of pretzels. Ted was anxious to find a headquarters, because the division was close behind. They were scouting for a large building on enough land to hold thirty large military vehicles and many more small ones in a protected location. Such would be preferable to pitching tents in an open field.

They came upon such a place without much difficulty in the suburban outskirts of Garmisch, at Zoeppritzstrasse 42: a large three-story mansion in a spacious glade surrounded by tall trees, nestled in the Loisach Valley of the Bavarian Alps. The view of the Zugspitze, Germany's highest mountain, was magnificent. According to protocol, Major Kramers waited in the jeep while Sgt. Greiss approached the villa and knocked on the front door. A tall, straight-backed, courtly man wearing a jacket and tie opened the door and spoke in good English. Sgt. Greiss politely requested that he and the other occupants of the house come out and talk to Major Kramers. Ted respectfully asked the man and his family to leave in twenty minutes with any possessions they would need, so that the Americans could temporarily occupy the villa.

When Ted and Sgt. Griess returned to the villa about thirty minutes later, the owner led them into a large salon with a piano and served tea and cakes. Ted thought him to be an unusually gentle and modest man, especially compared with other Germans he had encountered during his brief sojourn in Germany. The man sat at the piano and played excerpts from *Der Rosenkavalier*. By then, Ted, a reluctant violin student in his

Philadelphia school days, realized that the owner of the villa was none other than Richard Strauss.

Ted was introduced to a younger woman, probably Strauss's daughter-in-law, Alice, who served as his secretary: another man, probably Strauss's son, Franz; and another woman—Ted never learned her identity but she was probably Stauss's wife, Pauline. Far from the frail old man described by some commentators, Strauss appeared to Ted to be a healthy, sturdy, proud man who "still had all his marbles" despite his obvious advanced age (seventy-nine years).

Strauss had built the mansion in 1908 according to a design by himself, his wife, Pauline, and Emanuel von Seidl, brother of the architect of the Munich Museum. The family initially intended the villa to be a summer home, but after financial reverses—a British bank confiscated his assets after World War I—and during the rise of the Third Reich, they found refuge there, and a permanent residence. As the war worsened, Strauss's son and his family were forbidden to shop in Aryan shops and could not go out for fear of being beaten up. Strauss himself was spied on.

Strauss modestly described himself as "a first-class second-rate composer" and was listed in the Garmisch telephone directory (according to his friend, the tenor Hans Hotter) as "Dr. Strauss, Richard, Conductor" and not, as you might assume, "Composer."

At the time of Ted's visit, Strauss was arranging *Der Rosenkavalier*, an opera he had written many years earlier, as a suite for orchestra, in part to produce a legacy of value for his family. The image of Strauss's fingers on the piano keys stayed with Ted, and he always sat in the front row at our concerts for just that reason.

The encounter was short, because Ted was ready to take possession of the house.

Ted doesn't know where the Strauss family went that day, but believes that they learned within hours that they could return immediately: The Army was ahead of schedule and passed through the town without stopping. Neither Ted nor any other Americans ever occupied the villa.

After the war, having briefly accepted the post of head of the Reich Music Chamber (probably without an opportunity to decline—and, he believed, "to do good and prevent even greater misfortune"), Strauss was automatically classified as "Grade I Guilty" by a denazification court and lost more of his assets. Many of his musician contemporaries treated him with contempt, because he remained in Germany during the war and even conducted for the Nazi elite. (Toscanini said, "To Strauss the musician I take off my hat; to Strauss the man I put it on again.") In 1948 he was exonerated and reinstated as a German citizen. By then he and his family were living in exile in Switzerland, where he wrote his exquisite *Four Last Songs* and *Metamorphosen*. He and his family returned to the villa in Garmisch several months before he died there in September 1949. Pauline passed away in 1950. The grandchildren still maintain the home.

Other, more welcome, knocks at the same door about that time came from American musicians stationed with Army bands in the area. One of them, Dave Brubeck, wrote to me and I'm sure to others: "I was stationed in the Army at Eibsee near Oberammergau, and often would pass by Richard Strauss' home. I never had the nerve to go knock at his door, although I wanted to." Pittsburgh Symphony [later Philadelphia] oboist John de Lancie did knock. The eventual result was the *Oboe Concerto* that Strauss completed later in the year in Switzerland.

Ted Kramers received more publicity a few weeks later, thanks to his participation in one of the many "liberation parties" that roamed the countryside looking to free famous captives. His party freed ex-premiers Daladier and Raymond, De Gaulle's sister, and Generals Gamelin and Weygand from the prison castle of Itter, a high-class branch of Dachau used to lock up important prisoners. They "weren't merely out for sport," according to Meyer Levin, who traveled with one of the liberating units. "They went out in advance of their main elements because one day was often the margin needed for rescue. To the very last, the Germans were dragging important prisoners to the remotest mountains."

We will all miss Ted.

The conductor led soloists and orchestra in a well-paced reading of the 5th Brandenburg Concerto which, if not stunning, was at least not troublesome either, save one glitch: the first movement harpsichord cadenza slowed the pace too far out of proportion for comfort, reducing the thrilling cadenza to a tepid interlude.

— music critic in Lancaster, PA

27

THE RUBATO QUEEN
OF SHAKER HEIGHTS

It seems likely that music critics have aroused the contempt of musicians ever since shepherds in the ancient Arcadian hills told the god Pan what they thought of his piping on the syrinx. In the pidgin poetry of the outspoken conductor Sir Thomas Beecham, a regular target of London critics, critics were "quite hopeless—drooling, doleful, depressing, dropsical droops." "Feuilletonists," wrote the volatile composer Hector Berlioz about most French music critics, "obliged to write on anything and everything within the domain of their feuilleton (a gloomy domain, bog-ridden, infested with toads and grasshoppers) . . ."

To the argument that music critics are failed performers who criticize their more talented competitors, critic Martin Bernheimer replies, "You don't have to be able to lay an egg to know if you've been served a rotten one." So although some still consider critics members of the world's second oldest profession, the rest of us might adopt the more tempered view of poet James Russell Lowell, who found "wise skepticism" among good critics of all types. Critics like Samuel Lipman and Charles Rosen come to mind. Many notable examples, however, prove that even the best critics can be miserably wrong. "It stinks to the ear," wrote the powerful Viennese critic Eduard Hanslick after an early performance of Tchaikovsky's *Violin Concerto*—maybe while suffering an unusually severe case of synesthesia—before it became one of the most famous concertos of all time. George Bernard Shaw labeled Brahms a "Leviathan Maunderer."

As an occasional professional flutist, I have never been panned by a captious critic, maybe because I don't play in New York City, where the most sophisticated ones lurk. They feast on a more bountiful musical banquet than their gentler colleagues in smaller communities, who tend to report rather than criticize. So as one of the soloists mentioned by the small-town critic quoted above, I was startled by the words "tepid interlude."

Our critic, however, was on the mark.

Although the flute and violin are also solo instruments in Bach's *Fifth Brandenburg Concerto*, the work is actually the first keyboard concerto with orchestra ever written. The harpsichord cadenza in the first movement, marked *solo senza stromenti* (harpsichord alone), is a three-minute explosion of notes demanding immense virtuosity. Doris Ornstein, our harpsichordist, had played it brilliantly throughout an illustrious career. But that night, both critic and audience were unaware of an important reality.

For a flutist who loves the music of Bach, a harpsichordist is an essential collaborator. So after hearing Doris play at a prestigious concert series at the Cleveland Museum of Art, I had mustered my courage, walked the two blocks between my office at University Hospitals and her studio at the Cleveland Institute of Music, and introduced myself. Although I had set aside only thirty minutes for my visit, hours raced by as we discovered shared interests as well as overlapping circles of musician friends. Those who know me will correctly suspect that Doris did most of the talking: Her chatter flowed like an elaborately ornamented Bach *corrente*.* In time, I learned that bubbling, loquacious good humor and boundless energy were among Doris's endearing qualities, along with a delightful mischief that came out unexpectedly in both her conversation and her playing. These traits earned her, among friends and in honor of her hometown, the whimsical sobriquet "The Rubato Queen of Shaker

* A lively Italian dance.

Heights." Invoking her nickname always enlivened even the most tedious rehearsal.*

Our first meeting led to dozens of performances with our musician friends in several states. We played a gamut of cantatas, sonatas, and concertos and even three oratorios, bringing me close to my dream of learning and performing all of Bach's music that includes the flute: perhaps an easier goal than acting in all of Shakespeare's plays, but a similar one. I learned a lot from Doris about music and the joy of making it. I also learned to drive with the nose of a harpsichord inserted between the front seats, blocking the radio dials and gearshift like a large sleeping Labrador retriever. Most harpsichords played today are exact replicas of a particular Flemish, French, or Italian ancestor. With uncanny foresight, seventeenth-century harpsichord makers anticipated the dimensions of a late twentieth-century full-sized station wagon with barely an inch to spare!

Four years after our first meeting, Doris had a seizure on a flight to a concert tour in Europe and had to withdraw from the tour. Doctors in Amsterdam were puzzled after viewing a non-contrast CT scan, but after she returned home, my colleagues in our hospital made the diagnosis: a glioma (tumor) in the right temporal lobe. The tumor was resected—a palliative measure only. Radiotherapy and then chemotherapy were administered. Doris began to recover. Her wig hardly altered her appearance because it perfectly matched the impish cut of her natural hair, with bangs in the front down to her eyebrows.

Phenytoin (to prevent seizures) made her feel tired and sluggish, but that problem improved after substitution of carbamazepine. She had no more seizures. Her intellect, mobility, and language all emerged intact, and her *correntes* were slower and less effervescent only to those who knew her well. Preparing for rehearsals of the next concert, she was, as always, concerned with details, including the necessity of restoring a single measure in a Bach sonata omitted by most publishers since Bach's

---

* Literally, "stealing time" in one part of a phrase—by slowing or speeding up—that then must be made up within the same or next measure in order to maintain the same tempo. Chopin was a master of rubato.

time. Her letters, after I had moved away from Cleveland, were as legible and fluent as before—though I noticed that every left margin, although very straight, ran diagonally down the page, increasing from a half inch at the top to almost three inches at the bottom. That problem appeared even on her "Flemish Flamboyant" stationery with its florid two-inch rococo pattern—the kind that lined the keyboard wells of old harpsichords—surrounding the writing space.

Doris resumed her teaching and then her performance schedule, albeit at a slower pace. Bob, her husband, now accompanied her on tours, "to see," she said, "that I don't rehearse more than four hours at a time." ("To move the harpsichord," he said, tactfully.) In rehearsals she was not especially troubled by a visual defect that wanted to hide the left side of her keyboard and music. The lid of the harpsichord, like that of the piano, is hinged on the left of the keyboard, and the audience is to the performer's right. We positioned the other musicians and the conductor to Doris's right as well.

Because Doris had learned most of the repertoire for her instrument before her illness, I can't say how it affected her ability to learn new music. Everything she knew, even the cadenza from the *Fifth Brandenburg Concerto*, she could still play perfectly, but at a slower and more deliberate pace. What she and her playing had lost was some of the sparkle, fluidity, spontaneity—and rubato—that had made Doris and her music unique and extraordinary.

The concert attended by the critic was the last concert Doris was to play. Even though an assistant played part of the program, Doris had to rest often in rehearsals. But she was revitalized by friends and family, and especially by her daughter, Suzanne, a professional violinist who came from New York for this first and only opportunity to perform in public with her mother. It was a bittersweet occasion for the musicians, the terror of something going wrong mixed with gratitude for the opportunity to make music with Doris one more time.

On the night of the concert, a capacity audience filled a majestic eighteenth-century church in Lancaster, Pennsylvania. As the critic wrote, the performance of the Brandenburg Concerto, last on the program, was indeed "not stunning," but it was good. Few in the audience were so critical: Most were captivated by the rich sounds of great music in an acoustically wonderful space, the vitality of the playing, and the chance to see and hear an exotic, highly decorated harpsichord played by a great artist. A standing ovation showed that, despite the "tepid interlude," we had touched almost everyone. It was indeed a glorious twilight of the career of a remarkable and courageous lady and great musician. Sometime afterwards, the *corrente* flowed to its final rest.

Fig. 7. The author with Doris

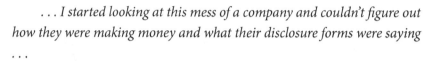

. . . I started looking at this mess of a company and couldn't figure out how they were making money and what their disclosure forms were saying . . .

—Richard Conniff, "The Fraud Detective," *Yale Alumni Magazine*, September/October 2013

28
MY ILLUSTRIOUS CAREER
AS A NON-PIANIST

I have never lived in a house without a piano: For me that would be like having a living room without a sofa or a kitchen without a refrigerator. When I was in the third grade, a portly piano teacher, Mrs. Reeder, always dressed in black, began arriving weekly to teach me to play my mother's Hardman & Peck Eavestaff Minipiano. Even at that young age, I wondered whether piano keys meant anything more to her than those on my dad's old Underwood mechanical typewriter. Her wooden ruler whacked any fingers on the wrong keys. After a humiliating public recital, when all but the first two measures of "Around the Campfire" deserted me repeatedly, she decided to bestow her skills elsewhere. But I did learn how to read music, and emerged from the ordeal with perfect pitch (only for the Minipiano, because I was about eight years old at the time, and my critical period for developing absolute pitch had passed). But I could read music, so I was in better shape to start lessons on the flute in the fifth grade and to learn Latin in the ninth.

Part of my attraction for the flute was that fifth-grade band members got to leave class twice a week, plus most of the other flute players were girls, a definite advantage when I got older. I gave too little credit to Harlan Thomas ("Mr. Thomas"), the band director who guided me all the way through to the eleventh grade, when I quit the band because I didn't like marching, even with a piccolo I could carry in my pocket. Not long afterwards, Mr. Thomas decided that real estate would be a better career for him if he ever wanted to retire. He was in the vanguard of a trend among music teachers escaping to better-paying careers. I wish I had been able to tell him how much he changed my life.

A Hamburg Steinway came with my first wife, after she had traveled the world with her father on his foreign-service assignments. Then, inexplicably, I built (in between thirty-six-hour shifts as a medical intern) a small spinet harpsichord from a kit: on the kitchen table, just as the kit manufacturer promised could be done. I preferred the harpsichord as an accompaniment for Bach flute sonatas, and it easily fit in the back seat for my gigs at weddings. Fifty years later it still plays perfectly and serves as a reliable continuo (bass accompaniment) for performances of Baroque music.

Just after I started my first job at Penn State's Medical Center in Hershey, Pennsylvania, I outbid an incredulous piano dealer for an ancient Bechstein grand, abandoned in a dark, dusty room of a defunct small private school in Philadelphia. Guest pianists at Gretna still praise it, with its new pinblock and sound board, when warming up in my library before concerts. That was soon followed by building a replica of Mozart's favorite Andreas Stein fortepiano from another kit sold by Phillip Belt, who lived in a forest in Battleground, Indiana. Its sound was too weak, however, to balance the sound of a modern metal flute. Next I built a large, two-manual French harpsichord from a Hubbard kit, for my wife to play at Baroque concerts. I had to buy a station wagon to transport that. It is a beautiful instrument that we used for a Brandenburg Concerto with the Harrisburg Symphony, for music at the Pennsylvania Governor's Mansion, and later at a dinner for Penn State's most distinguished professors (all men). They saw what I had been doing instead of working in my medical lab.

All those instruments finally required Leroy, an Amish carpenter, to build (in two days, with his entire family) a large new room on one end of my small cottage that later came in handy for rehearsals of Mozart piano concertos and Dvorak serenades. The next owners of the house replaced my driveway sign, "No Turns," with a new one: "The Music House."

I married again and my wife came with a new Baldwin grand, just before that company self-destructed (more on the Baldwin story below). My final acquisition was an old 1923 Aeolian small grand, its original player mechanism excised by an aggressive surgeon years ago. A tuner and I rolled it down the road in the Palm Springs, California, desert, on a dolly from a neighbor's house to ours. Luckily for piano movers and bicycling seniors, the streets in Palm Springs are mostly flat. Our winter house in the desert just hadn't felt like a home without a piano.

I have played in orchestras behind many great pianists, like Arthur Rubinstein and Van Cliburn. I often wish, as do so many others I know, that I had taken the piano more seriously in childhood (though I now realize that the piano would never have taken *me* seriously). At the same time, I am grateful that the flute is far less all-consuming and demanding, enough so that I could manage reasonably successful careers in both medicine and music throughout my life. Had I aspired to be a pianist, I would soon have been consigned to amateur status.

Gretna Music has hosted almost one hundred pianists over forty-two years, including Leon Fleisher, Emanuel Ax, and Garrick Ohlsson. At first we rented pianos from a Lebanon, Pennsylvania, piano dealer, inexplicably located on the *second* floor of a nineteenth-century building and overseen by an ancient and irascible German proprietor named Herr Reifsnyder. I first thought the place must have branched off from the Wieck Piano factory in Leipzig, but then found that most of the pianos had Japanese names. Their legs punctured the rotting floors of the old Gretna Playhouse, and felt came unglued from hammers at the most inopportune times.

Then, in 1982, we rented a majestic Baldwin concert grand, because our schedule included Dave Brubeck at the beginning of the season, Marian McPartland in the middle, and George Shearing at the end. I, and they, were quite happy with the instrument, and it cost only slightly more than a small BMW. That was when the late, great gastroenterologist Bob Dye served on our board. I can't even begin to imagine the conversation he must have had with one of his elderly musically inclined patients lying helpless on his examining table, but she bought the piano for us. (I have always hoped there was no sigmoidoscope involved.) The big Baldwin has served with distinction for almost forty years, and has proud scars to prove it.

And yet, it happens often. At the reception after a concert, the pianist quietly, confidentially, and as if the words were about to come as a revelation from heaven, says to me, "You ought to get a Steinway." Our Baldwin has been the butt of harsh comments from dozens of pianists, especially when we get behind in maintenance—and that can be a challenge out here in the humid and often hot Gretna forest. But we never fail to tune and tweak it right before a concert, even if there is only one short piano work on the program. Most pianists have liked, or at least tolerated, it. I can think of better ways that $125,000 could improve our music at Gretna than by replacing a Baldwin with a Steinway, but that's a non-issue anyway, because we will never face that luxurious choice.

You may have noticed that pianos (must we now call them "acoustic pianos"?) have lost more value than a 1959 Plymouth (let alone books and records). Most without a Steinway decal (except for a few rare ones, like Bösendorfer and Fazioli) are worth roughly their weight in garden mulch.

The Steinway company remains strong and proud —as they should be, especially in light of the story of how Baldwin left the stage. I read a version of the story by Richard Conniff:

> Baldwin was a piano company that had transformed itself, by a series of acquisitions, into an insurance giant and Wall Street darling. When it announced its latest acquisition in the summer of 1982, Jim Chanos [a Yale professor and investment analyst, and the subject of the article] got the job of figuring out if the proposed deal would be good [for his investment clients]. "And I started looking at this mess of a company and couldn't figure out how they were making money and what their disclosure forms were saying..."

Then one night … his phone rang…[An anonymous caller] proceeded to point Chanos to public files of correspondence between Baldwin and state insurance regulators in Arkansas. Those files turned out to be a beginner's guide to financial she-nanigans. The regulators had belatedly discovered, among other things, that Baldwin was improperly using insurance reserves to finance its acquisitions.[288]

Four months later, Arkansas seized the assets of Baldwin-United, and Chanos became a celebrated financial detective who later uncovered scores of other financial shenanigans, including those of Enron, Tyco, Worldcom, and the subprime mortgage mess.

You can find a more comprehensive version of the Baldwin story on Wikipedia and elsewhere; but the company, now a subsidiary of the Gibson Guitar Company, makes pianos, mostly uprights I suppose, in China (a country, according to Chanos, "on an economic treadmill to hell"[289]).

Now I appreciate our old Baldwin even more. It's old but has low mileage.

CONCLUSION

I hope you now have a little more than "a ghost of an idea about what music is, or why we make it and cannot be human without it," and understand "how the human mind makes music on its own, before it is written down and played."[290] Science has brought us closer to answering those questions, but it will take many more decades of research for more definitive answers. I also hope you will take away three important concepts from this book:

1. Musical Memory—a form of auditory memory, mostly inherited, possessed in the fullest extent only by humans;

2. Neuroplasticity—a quality necessary for learning and most robust in the first two decades of human life, and for attainment of some skills as early as possible; and

3. Connectivity—the billions of connections among all parts of the brain that we are born with and can manipulate with deliberate efforts and practice in order to become what we want to be and do what we want to do.

Learning and listening to music guides and depends on all these concepts. Studying how it does so teaches us about the brain and the human.

But I must admit that reading books about music can never substitute for listening to it—an unquestioned truth that says volumes about what music is. Listening to music should involve concentration, just as you would apply to reading a book. Enveloping yourself continually throughout the day in "an endless, shifting weather-cover of sound … a cloud in every sense, a perpetual availability of emotion to suit a mood and moment"[291] while carrying on other activities is not what I have in mind—even though an authority like Dan Levitin asserts that families who have music in their home make love more often.[292] (Probably he didn't mean constant wall-to-wall sound, though.) I have friends who turn on their music radio station when they get out of bed and turn it off only just before getting back into bed at night. Doing what they do would only distract me from what I am trying to accomplish, however, and wouldn't allow me to fully respond to the music. Instead, I take breaks from daily activity, recline on the sofa, and carefully select what I want to listen to for the next hour or so. I especially like to listen to music during long solitary drives in the car. Or I buy I ticket to a live performance, because music is something that humans have always enjoyed with other humans, until the advent of recordings and earbuds.

That said, and though you don't have to study the history of navigation or boat building to sail a boat, it helps to know, from books perhaps, how to set the sail and orient the boat to the wind. The fullest enjoyment of music, as of any art or science, depends on experience, knowledge, and context. I hope I have successfully shared some of those aspects of my life in music with you. I wish I had begun music study even earlier than I did, because I am convinced—as I tried to convince *you*—that if you learn music early, just as you learn your native language, you prepare yourself to learn anything else more easily and deeply and enjoy a richer life.

As for Adam Gopnik, so for me: "Music meant difficulty—and, when the difficulty was overcome, the possibilities of life, too. It was something to master."[293]

Endnotes

1. Lewis Thomas, *On Matters of Doubt: Late Night Thoughts on Listening to Mahler's Ninth Symphony* (New York, Viking Press, 1980), p. 162. The author named his collection of essays for the darkest in the group.

2. Edward O. Wilson, *The Meaning of Human Existence* (New York, Liveright Publishing Corp., a Division of W.W. Norton & Company, 2014), p. 148.

3. Aniruddh D. Patel, "Music, Biological Evolution, and the Brain," in *Emerging Disciplines*, ed. M. Bailar (Houston, TX: Rice University Press, 2010), p. 3.

4. Neil A. Busis, et al., Burnout, Career Satisfaction, and Well-Being among US Neurologists in 2016," *Neurology* 88 (2017): 797-808.

5. Kevin N. Laland, *Darwin's Unfinished Symphony; How Culture Made the Human Mind* (Princeton, NJ: Princeton University Press, 2017), p. 37.

6. Oliver Sacks, *Musicophilia: Tales of Music and the Brain* (New York: Vintage Books, 2008).

7. Adam Gopnik, "Music to Your Ears," *The New Yorker*, January 28, 2013, p. 33.

8. Peter Wohlleben, *The Hidden Life of Trees: What They Feel, How They Communicate* (Vancouver, BC: Greystone Books, 2016).

9. Leonard Bernstein, *The Unanswered Question: Six Talks at Harvard* (West Long Branch, NJ: Kultur International Films, 1973), www.kultur. com.

10. Deryck Cooke, *The Language of Music* (London: Oxford University

Press, 1959).

11. Aniruddh D. Patel, *Music, Language, and the Brain* (New York, Oxford University Press, 2008).

12. Anthony Brandt, Molly Gebrian, and L. Robert Slevc, "Music and Early Language Acquisition," *Frontiers in Psychology* 3, article 327 (September 2012).

13. Ian Bostridge, "God's Own Music," *The New York Review of Books*, February 22, 2018. "Her voice was a thread," wrote Charles Burney, the eighteenth-century music chronicler, "and her knowledge of Music very inconsiderable, yet by a natural pathos, and a perfect conception of the words, she often penetrated the heart, when others, with infinitely greater voice and skill, could only reach the ear."

14. T. S. Eliot, "Tradition and the Individual Talent," in *Selected Essays*, 1917–1932 (New York: Harcourt Brace, 1932). "It involves, in the first place, the historical sense, which we may call nearly indispensable to any one who would continue to be a poet beyond his twenty-fifth year; and the historical sense involves a perception, not only of the pastness of the past, but of its presence; the historical sense compels a man to write not merely with his own generation in his bones, but with a feeling that the whole of the literature of Europe from Homer and within it the whole of the literature of his own country has a simultaneous existence and composes a simultaneous order."

15. Gopnik, p. 32.

16. Richard Taruskin, "The Modern Sound of Early Music," in *Text and Act: Essays on Music and Performance* (New York: Oxford University Press, 1995), p. 166.

17. K. Anders Ericsson, "Deliberate Practice and the Acquisition and Maintenance of Expert Performance in Medicine and Related Domains," *Academic Medicine* 79:10 (October 2004): S70–81.

18. Maria Popova, "The Silent Music of the Mind: Remembering Oliver Sacks" (2015), at https://www.brainpickings.org/20 https://brainpickings.us2.list-manage.com/track/click?u=13eb080d8a315477042e0d-5b1&id=622c8d006d&e=81c44f77ff15/08/31/remembering-oliver-sacks/.

19. Edward O. Wilson, *The Meaning of Human Existence,* p. 147.

20. Josh McDermott and Marc D. Hauser, "Nonhuman Primates Prefer Slow Tempos but Dislike Music Overall," *Cognition*;104 (2007): 654–68.

21. Brian H. Scott, Mortimer Mishkin, and Pingbo Yin, "Monkeys Have a Limited Form of Short-Term Memory in Audition," *Proceedings of the National Academy of Sciences of the United States of America* 109(30)

(2012): 12237–41.

22. Thomas Higham et al., "Testing Models for the Beginnings of the Aurignacian and the Advent of Figurative Art and Music: The Radiocarbon Chronology of Geißenklösterle," *Journal of Human Evolution* 62(6) (2012): 664–76.

23. Ann M. MacLarnon and Gwen P. Hewitt, "The Evolution of Human Speech: The Role of Enhanced Breathing Control," *American Journal of Physical Anthropology* 1999;109 (1999): 341–63.

24. Steven Mithen, "Our 86 Billion Neurons: She Showed it," review of *The Human Advantage*, by Suzana Herculano-Houzel, *The New York Review of Books*, November 24, 2016, pp. 42–44.

25. Ray Jackendoff and Fred Lerdahl, "The Capacity for Music: What Is It, and What's Special about It?" *Cognition* 100 (2006): 33–72.

26. Jaana Oikkonen et al., "Convergent Evidence for the Molecular Basis of Musical Traits," *Scientific Reports* 6, article number 39707 (2016); Jaana Oikkonen et al., "Creative Activities in Music: A Genome-Wide Linkage Analysis," *PLoS One* 11(2) (2016): e0148679; and Spencer Wells, *The Journey of Man: A Genetic Odyssey* (Princeton, NJ: Princeton University Press, 2003).

27. Lewis Thomas, p. 149.

28. Howard H. Cox, ed., *The Calov Bible of J. S. Bach* (Studies in Musicology, no. 92) (Ann Arbor, MI: UMI Research Press, 1986), p. 418.

29. David Huron, "Is Music an Evolutionary Adaptation?" *Annals of the New York Academy of Sciences* 930, Issue 1 (2001): 43–61; and Charles T. Snowdon, Elke Zimmermann, and Eckart Altenmüller, "Music Evolution and Neuroscience," *Progress in Brain Research* 217C (March 2015): 17–34.

30. Bernie Krause, *The Great Animal Orchestra: Finding the Origins of Music in the World's Wild Places* (New York: Little, Brown, 2012).

31. Steven Pinker, *How the Mind Works* (New York: Norton, 1997), p. 528. "As far as biological cause and effect are concerned," writes Pinker, "music is useless."

32. Peter-Jan Maes, "Sensorimotor Grounding of Musical Embodiment and the Role of Prediction: A Review," *Frontiers in Psychology* 7 (March 4, 2016): 308.

33. Steve Paulson et al., "Music and the Mind: The Magical Power of Sound," *Annals of the New York Academy of Sciences* 1303 (November 2013): 63–79.

34. Edward O. Wilson, *The Meaning of Human Existence*, p.148.

35. Michael A. Ferguson et al., "Reward, Salience, and Attentional

Networks Are Activated by Religious Experience in Devout Mormons," *Social Neuroscience* 13(1) (2018): 104–16.

36. Charles T. Snowdon, Elke Zimmermann, and Eckart Altenmüller, "Music Evolution and Neuroscience".

37. Samuel A. Mehr et al., "Form and Function in Human Song," *Current Biology* 28(3) (February 2018): 356–68, e5.

38. Stacy Horn, *Imperfect Harmony: Finding Happiness Singing with Others* (Chapel Hill, NC: Algonquin Books, 2013).

39. Kevin N. Laland, *Darwin's Unfinished Symphony*, p. 264

40. Snowdon, Zimmermann, and Altenmüller, "Music Evolution and Neuroscience".

41. Alfred R. Wallace, *Contributions to the Theory of Natural Selection: A Series of Essays* (London: Macmillan, 1870).

42. Kevin N. Laland, *Darwin's Unfinished Symphony*, p. 13.

43. Robert Boyd, *A Different Kind of Animal: How Culture Transformed Our Species* (Princeton, NJ: Princeton University Press, 2017); and Laland, *Darwin's Unfinished Symphony*.

44. Kevin N. Laland, *Darwin's Unfinished Symphony*, p. 13.

45. Ibid, p. 26.

46. Ibid, p. 17.

47. Ibid, Chapter 1.

48. Ibid, p. 206.

49. Ibid, p. 201.

50. Jerrold Levinson, "Musical Frissons," *Revue française d'études américaines*, no. 86 (October 2000): 6476.

51. Edward O. Wilson, *The Meaning of Human Existence*, p. 147.

52. Robert J. Zatorre, "Musical Pleasure and Reward: Mechanisms and Dysfunction," *Annals of the New York Academy of Sciences* 1337(1) (March 2015): 202–11.

53. Luke Harrison and Psyche Loui, "Thrills, Chills, Frissons, and Skin Orgasms: Toward an Integrative Model of Transcendent Psychophysiological Experiences in Music," *Frontiers in Psychology* 5 (2014): 3, https://pdfs.semanticscholar.org/7ae3/f2cdbb0a40a2757ea5b-1c8a66232f4d9e77e.pdf .

54. Matthew E. Sachs et al., "Brain Connectivity Reflects Human Aesthetic Responses to Music," *Social Cognitive and Affective Neuroscience* 11(6) (June 2016): 884–91.

55. Harrison and Loui, "Thrills, Chills, Frissons, and Skin Orgasms: Toward an Integrative Model of Transcendent Psychophysiological Experiences in Music".

56. Matthew E. Sachs et al., "Brain Connectivity Reflects Human Aesthetic Responses to Music"; and Noelia Martinez-Molina et al., "Neural Correlates of Specific Musical Anhedonia," *Proceedings of the National Academy of Sciences of the United States of America* 113(46) (November 15, 2016): E7337–E7345.

57. Adiel Mallik, Mona Lisa Chanda, and Daniel J. Levitin, "Anhedonia to Music and Mu-opioids: Evidence from the Administration of Naltrexone," *Scientific Reports* 7, article number41952 (2017).

58. Paul Elie, *Reinventing Bach* (New York: Farrar, Straus and Giroux, 2012).

59. Isabelle Peretz and Max Coltheart, "Modularity of Music Processing," *Nature Neuroscience* 6, no. 7 (July 2003): 688–91.

60. Robert J. Zatorre and Valorie N. Salimpoor, "From Perception to Pleasure: Music and Its Neural Substrates," *Proceedings of the National Academy of Sciences of the United States of America* 110(Suppl 2) (June 18, 2013): 10430–37.

61. Patel, "Music, Biological Evolution, and the Brain".

62. Ibid.

63. E. Glenn Schellenberg, "Exposure to Music: The Truth about the Consequences," in *The Child as Musician: A Handbook of Musical Development*, ed. Gary E. McPherson (New York: Oxford University Press; 2006), pp. 111–34; and E. Glenn Schellenberg, "Music Lessons Enhance IQ," *Psychological Science* 15, issue 8 (2004): 511–14.

64. Margaret Allen, "People who deeply grasp the pain or happiness of others also process music differently in the brain." http://blog.smu.edu/research/2018/06/11/people-who-deeply-grasp-the-pain-or-happiness-of-others-also-process-music-differently-in-the-brain/. The authors discuss their research report: Zachary Wallmark, Choi Deblieck, and Marco Iacoboni, "Neurophysiological Effects of Trait Empathy in Music Listening," Frontiers in Behavioral Neuroscience, 12 (April 6, 2018):6.

65. William Weber, The Great Transformation of Musical Taste: Concert Programming from Haydn to Brahms (New York: Cambridge University Press, 2008). See esp. Chapter 3: "Musical idealism and the crisis of the old order," pp. 85—121.

66. Alex Ross, "The Musical Kaleidoscope," *The New Yorker* August 26, 1996.

67. Eckart Altenmüller and Gottfried Schlaug, "Apollo's Gift: New Aspects of Neurologic Music Therapy," *Progress in Brain Research* 217 (2015): 237–52; and Gottfried Schlaug, "Musicians and Music Making as a Model for the Study of Brain Plasticity," *Progress in Brain Research*

217 (2015): 37–55.

68. Jacob Kwalwasser, *Exploring the Musical Mind* (New York: Coleman-Ross, 1955), p. 9.

69. K. Anders Ericsson, Ralf Th. Krampe, and Clemens Tesch-Römer, "The Role of Deliberate Practice in the Acquisition of Expert Performance," *Psychological Review* 100, no. 3 (1993): 363–406.

70. Levinson, "Musical Frissons".

71. Eckart Altenmüller, Christos I. Ioannou, and André Lee, "Apollo's Curse: Neurological Causes of Motor Impairments in Musicians," *Progress in Brain Research* 217C (2015): 89–106.

72. Francis Collins, "The Symphony Inside Your Brain," NIH Director's Blog, November 5, 2012, https://directorsblog.nih.gov/?s=Symphony&submit=Search.

73. Christian Gaser and Gottfried Schlaug, "Gray Matter Differences between Musicians and Nonmusicians," *Annals of the New York Academy of Sciences* 999 (2003): 514–17.

74. Sioban Hutchinson, et al., "Cerebellar Volume of Musicians," *Cerebral Cortex* 13(9) (September 2003): 943–49.

75. Marcus Herdener et al., "Musical Training Induces Functional Plasticity in Human Hippocampus," *Journal of Neuroscience* 30(4) (January 27, 2010): 1377–84.

76. Gottfried Schlaug et al., "Increased Corpus Callosum Size in Musicians," *Neuropsychologia* 33(8) (August 1995): 1047–55; and Catherine Y. Wan and Gottfried Schlaug, "Music Making as a Tool for Promoting Brain Plasticity across the Life Span," *Neuroscientist* 16(5) (October 2010): 566–77.

77. Gus F. Halwani et al., "Effects of Practice and Experience on the Arcuate Fasciculus: Comparing Singers, Instrumentalists, and Non-musicians," *Frontiers in Psychology* 2 (July 7, 2011): 156.

78. Sam Norman-Haignere, Nancy G. Kanwisher, and Josh H. McDermott, "Distinct Cortical Pathways for Music and Speech Revealed by Hypothesis-Free Voxel Decomposition," *Neuron* 88(6) (December 16, 2015): 1281–96.

79. Norman Geschwind, "Disconnexion Syndromes in Animals and Man. II," *Brain* 88(3) (September 1965): 585–644.

80. David B. Fischer et al., "A Human Brain Network Derived from Coma-Causing Brainstem Lesions," *Neurology* 87(23) (December 2016): 2427–34.

81. David Brang, Lisa E. Williams, Vilayanur S. Ramachandran, "Grapheme-color synesthetes show enhanced crossmodal processing

between auditory and visual modalities," *Cortex* 48(5) (May 2012): 630-7.

82. Katie Womack, "Hélène Grimaud on Brahms, Synesthesia and a Passion for Wolves," *Dallas Observer*, January 16, 2014, http://www.dallasobserver.com/arts/h-l-ne-grimaud-on-brahms-synesthesia-and-a-passion-for-wolves-7092407.

83. Amanda K. Tilot, Katerina S. Kucera, Arianna Vino, et al. Rare gene variants in axonogenesis genes connect three families with sound-color synesthesia, *Proceedings of the National Academy of Sciences of the United States of America* 115(12) (March 2018): 3168-3173.

84. Gina Shaw, "Unlocking the Genetic Basis of Synesthesia," *Neurology Today* 18(8) (April 19, 2018):20, Quoting Vilayanur Ramachandran.

85. Diana Deutsch, "The Enigma of Absolute Pitch," *Acoustics Today*;2 (October 2006): 11-18.

86. Siamak Baharloo et al., "Absolute Pitch: An Approach for Identification of Genetic and Nongenetic Components," *American Journal of Human Genetics* 62(2) (February 1998): 224–31.

87. Deutsch, "The Enigma of Absolute Pitch".

88. Julie Ayotte, Isabelle Peretz, and Krista Hyde, "Congenital Amusia: A Group Study of Adults Afflicted with a Music-Specific Disorder," *Brain* 125(2) (February 2002): 238–51.

89. Oliver Sacks, *Musicophilia*, p. 108-109.

90. Hans Kalmus and Dennis B. Fry, "On Tune Deafness (Dysmelodia): Frequency, Development, Genetics and Musical Background," *Annals of Human Genetics*;43 (May 1980): 369–82.

91. Dennis Drayna et al., "Genetic Correlates of Musical Pitch Recognition in Humans," *Science* 291(5510) (March 9, 2001): 1969–72.

92. Psyche Loui, Anna Zamm, and Gottfried Schlaug, "Enhanced Functional Networks in Absolute Pitch," *Neuroimage* 63(2) (November 1, 2012): 632–40.

93. Peter K. Gregersen et al., "Absolute Pitch Exhibits Phenotypic and Genetic Overlap with Synesthesia," *Human Molecular Genetics* 22(10) (May 15, 2013): 2097–104.

94. David Hajdu, Forever Young? In Some Ways, Yes *The New York Times*, May 23, 2011, quoting Daniel Levitin.

95. Elizabeth Brown and William R. Hendee, "Adolescents and Their Music. Insights into the Health of Adolescents," *JAMA* 262(12) (September 22–29, 1989): 1659–63.

96. Charles Rosen, *Freedom and the Arts: Essays on Music and Literature* (Cambridge: Harvard University Press, 2012), p. 16.

97. Josh H. McDermott et al., "Indifference to Dissonance in Native Amazonians Reveals Cultural Variation In Music Perception," *Nature* 535(7613) (July 28, 2016): 547–50.

98. Hillard Kaplan et al., "Coronary Atherosclerosis in Indigenous South American Tsimane: A Cross-sectional Cohort Study," *Lancet* 389(10080) (April 29, 2017): 1730–39.

99. Altenmüller and Schlaug, "Apollo's Gift: New Aspects of Neurologic Music Therapy".

100. Eric R. Kandel, *In Search of Memory: The Emergence of a New Science of Mind* (New York: Norton, 2006), pp. 91–94, citing pioneering work by Henry Dale, Otto Loewi, and Willam Feldberg.

101. Ibid., p. 65, citing four principles of the neuron doctrine formulated by Ramon y Cajal and discussing a modern interpretation.

102. Karen Chan Barrett et al., "Art and Science: How Musical Training Shapes the Brain," *Frontiers in Psychology* 4 (2013): 713.

103. Carina Klein et al., "The 'Silent' Imprint of Musical Training," *Human Brain Mapping* 37 (2016): 536–46.

104. Colin Blakemore and Richard C. Van Sluyters, "Reversal of the Physiological Effects of Monocular Deprivation in Kittens: Further Evidence for a Sensitive Period," *Journal of Physiology* 237(1) (February 1974): 195–216.

105. Virginia B. Penhune, "Sensitive Periods in Human Development: Evidence from Musical Training," *Cortex* 47(9) (October 2011): 1126–37.

106. Thomas H. Bak et al., "Does Bilingualism Influence Cognitive Aging?" *Annals of Neurology* 75(6) (June 2014): 959–63.

107. Erika Skoe and Nina Kraus, "Musical Training Heightens Auditory Brainstem Function during Sensitive Periods in Development," *Frontiers in Psychology* 4 (2013): 622.

108. Alec Wilkinson, "Time is a Ghost: Vijay Iyer's Jazz Vision," *The New Yorker*, February 1, 2016.

109. Shunryu Suzuki, *Zen Mind, Beginner's Mind: Informal Talks on Zen Meditation and Practice* (Boulder: Shambhala, 2010).

110. Tania Singer, "I Feel Your Pain: The Social Neuroscience of Empathy and Compassion," in *The Monastery and the Microscope: Conversations with the Dalai Lama on Mind, Mindfulness, and the Nature of Reality*, ed. Wendy Hasenkamp and Janna R. White (New Haven: Yale University Press, 2017).

111. K. Anders Ericsson, Ralf T. Krampe, and Stefanie Heizmann, "Can We Create Gifted People?" Ciba Foundation Symposium 178 (February

1993): 178:222–31; discussion, 232–49. See also Ericsson, "Deliberate Practice and the Acquisition and Maintenance of Expert Performance"; Ericsson, Krampe, and Tesch-Römer, "The Role of Deliberate Practice in the Acquisition of Expert Performance".

112. Ibid.

113. Ibid.

114. Feras V. Akbik et al., "Anatomical Plasticity of Adult Brain Is Titrated by Nogo Receptor 1," *Neuron* 77(5) (March 6, 2013): 859–66.

115. Schellenberg, "Music Lessons Enhance IQ".

116. Nina Kraus and Travis White-Schwoch, "Neurobiology of Everyday Communication: What Have We Learned from Music?" *The Neuroscientist*, June 9, 2016, http://journals.sagepub.com/doi/full/10.1177/1073858416653593.

117. Jenni Laidman, "Music Helps Kids Read," *Scientific American* May 1, 2014, https://www.scientificamerican.com/article/music-helps-kids-read/.

118. Ibid.

119. Kraus and White-Schwoch, "Neurobiology of Everyday Communication: What Have We Learned from Music?"

120. Ingo Roden, Gunter Kreutz, and Stephan Bongard, "Effects of a School-Based Instrumental Music Program on Verbal and Visual Memory in Primary School Children: A Longitudinal Study," *Frontiers in Psychology* 3 (2012): 572.

121. Jennifer Zuk et al., "Behavioral and Neural Correlates of Executive Functioning in Musicians and Non-musicians," *PLoS One* 9(6) (2014): e99868.

122. E. Glenn Schellenberg, "Examining the Association between Music Lessons and Intelligence," *British Journal of Psychology* 102(3) (August 2011): 283–302; and Swathi Swaminathan, E. Glenn Schellenberg, and Safia Khalil, "Revisiting the Association between Music Lessons and Intelligence: Training Effects or Music Aptitude?" *Intelligence*, 62 (May 2017): 119–24.

123. Beatriz S. Ilari et al., "The Development of Musical Skills of Underprivileged Children Over the Course of 1 Year: A Study in the Context of an El Sistema–Inspired Program," *Frontiers in Psychology* 7 (2016): 62.

124. Assal Habibi et al., "Neural Correlates of Accelerated Auditory Processing in Children Engaged in Music Training," *Developmental Cognitive Neuroscience* 21 (October 2016): 1–14.

125. Matthew M. Sachs et al., "Increased Engagement of the Cognitive

Control Network Associated with Music Training in Children during an fMRI Stroop Task," *PLoS One* 12(10) (2017): e0187254.

126. Assal Habibi et al, "Childhood Music Training Induces Change in Micro and Macroscopic Brain Structure: Results from a Longitudinal Study," *Cerebral Cortex*, November 8, 2017: 1–12. doi: 10.1093/cercor/bhx286.

127. Ann McKee, "The Human Brain and Sports," *New York Times*, December 28, 2017, https://www.nytimes.com/interactive/2017/12/28/sports/cte-brains-concussions.html.

128. Byron Janis, "A Healing Art," *Wall Street Journal*, May 7, 2014.

129. http://www.yamahainstitute.org/a-new-perspective/. As he disclosed in the *Wall Street Journal*, Janis serves as Presidential Advisor for the Yamaha Music and Wellness Institute (YMWI). YMWI states that its "ultimate goal is to enable individuals of all ages, regardless of prior experience, to discover the joy and personal benefits of playing a musical instrument."

130. Ibrahim B. Syed, "Islamic Medicine: 1000 Years Ahead of Its Times," *Journal of the International Society for the History of Islamic Medicine* 2 (2002): 2–9. https://www.ishim.net/ishimj/2/01.pdf.

131. Peter F. Ostwald, with Lise Deschamps Ostwald, *Schumann: The Inner Voices of a Musical Genius*, new and expanded ed. (Boston: Northeastern University Press, 2010), p. 92.

132. Tor D. Wager, Lauren Y. Atlas, The neuroscience of placebo effects: connecting context, learning and health. *Nature Reviews. Neuroscience* 16(7) (July 2015): 403–18.

133. Scott W. Powers et al., "Trial of Amitriptyline, Topiramate, and Placebo for Pediatric Migraine," *New England Journal of Medicine* 376 (January 12, 2017): 115–24.

134. John Eliot Gardiner, "The Class of '85," in *Bach: Music in the Castle of Heaven* (New York, Knopf, 2013): p. 142.

135. Jeanette Sorrell, Artistic Direector, Apollo's Fire (The Cleveland Baroque Orchestra) website, https://apollosfire.org/about/apollos-fire/.

136. Marcia Angell, "The Illusions of Psychiatry," *New York Review of Books*, July 14, 2011 and Marcia Angell, "The Epidemic of Mental Illness: Why?" *New York Review of Books*, June 23, 2011.

137. Popova, "The Silent Music of the Mind: Remember Oliver Sacks".

138. Eduardo A. Garza-Villarreal et al., "Music-Induced Analgesia in Chronic Pain Conditions: A Systematic Review and Meta-Analysis," *Pain Physician* 20(7) (November 2017): 597–610.

139. http://www.yamahainstitute.org/a-new-perspective/.

140. Teppo Särkämö et al., "Music Listening Enhances Cognitive Recovery and Mood after Middle Cerebral Artery Stroke," *Brain: A Journal of Neurology* 131 (Pt. 3) (March 2008): 866–76.

141. Tobias Loetscher and Nadina B. Lincoln, "Cognitive Rehabilitation for Attention Deficits Following Stroke," Cochrane Database of Systematic Reviews (May 2013): 5(CD002842).

142. Catherine Y. Wan and Gottfried Schlaug, pp. 566-77.

143. Gottfried Schlaug, Sarah Marchina, and Andrea Norton, "From Singing to Speaking: Why Singing May Lead to Recovery of Expressive Language Function in Patients with Broca's Aphasia," *Music Perception* 25(4) (April 1, 2008): 315–23.

144. Eckart O. Altenmüller et al., "Neural Reorganization Underlies Improvement in Stroke-Induced Motor Dysfunction by Music-Supported Therapy," *Annals of the New York Academy of Sciences* 1169 (July 2009):395–405.

145. Antoni Rodriguez-Fornells et al., "The Involvement of Audio-Motor Coupling in the Music-Supported Therapy Applied to Stroke Patients," *Annals of the New York Academy of Sciences* 1252 (April 2012): 282–93.

146. Julia L. Amengual et al., "Sensorimotor Plasticity after Music-Supported Therapy in Chronic Stroke Patients Revealed by Transcranial Magnetic Stimulation," *PLoS One* 8(4) (April 17, 2013): e61883.

147. Vernon Pickles, "Musical Abilities May Outlast Other Faculties in Advanced Dementia," *Age and Ageing* 34(6) (November 2005): 655.

148. Vanessa Sluming et al., "Voxel-Based Morphometry Reveals Increased Gray Matter Density in Broca's Area in Male Symphony Orchestra Musicians," *Neuroimage* 17(3) (November 2002): 1613–22; and Janina Boyke et al., "Training-induced brain structure changes in the elderly. *Journal of Neuroscience* 28(28) (July 9, 2008): 7031–5.

149. Jessica V. Strong and Benjamin T. Mast, "The cognitive functioning of older adult instrumental musicians and non-musicians," *Neuropsychol Dev Cogn B Aging Neuropsychol Cogn.* (March 8, 2018): 1-20. Also: Jessica V. Strong and Allison Midden, "Cognitive differences between older adult instrumental musicians: Benefits of continuing to play," *Psychology of Music* (July 20, 2018).

150. Joe Verghese et al., "Leisure Activities and the Risk of Dementia in the Elderly," *New England Journal of Medicine* 348(25) (June 19, 2003): 2508–16.

151. J. A. Bugos et al., "Individualized Piano Instruction Enhances Executive Functioning and Working Memory in Older Adults," *Aging*

& Mental Health 11(4) (July 2007): 464–71; and Sofia Seinfeld et al., Effects of "Music Learning and Piano Practice on Cognitive Function, Mood and Quality of Life in Older Adults," *Frontiers in Psychology* 4 (November 1, 2013): 810.

152. Wan and Schlaug, pp. 566-77.

153. Robert S. Wilson et al., "Life-Span Cognitive Activity, Neuropathologic Burden, and Cognitive Aging," *Neurology* 81(4) (July 23, 2013): 314–21.

154. Prashanthi Vemuri and Elizabeth C. Mormino, "Cognitively Stimulating Activities to Keep Dementia at Bay," *Neurology* 81(4) (July 23, 2013): 308–9.

155. Wilson et al., "Life-Span Cognitive Activity."

156. Tarek Amer et al., "Do Older Professional Musicians Have Cognitive Advantages?" *PLoS One* 8(8) (August 7, 2013): e71630.

157. Bak et al. "Does Biligualism Influence Cognitive Aging?"

158. George W. Rebok et al., "Ten-Year Effects of the ACTIVE [Advanced Cognitive Training for Independent and Vital Elderly] Cognitive Training Trial on Cognition and Everyday Functioning in Older Adults," *Journal of the American Geriatrics Society* 62(1) (January 2014): 16–24.

159. *Preventing Cognitive Decline and Dementia: A Way Forward* (Report and video released June 22, 2017, by the National Academies of Sciences, Engineering and Medicine, ed. Autumn Downey, Clare Stroud, Story Landis, and Alan I. Leshner); see: http://nationalacademies.org/hmd/reports/2017/preventing-cognitive-decline-and-dementia-a-way-forward.aspx.

160. Helko Braak et al., "Staging of Brain Pathology Related to Sporadic Parkinson's Disease," *Neurobiology of Aging* 24(2) (March–April 2003): 197–211.

161. Miriam R. Rafferty et al., "Regular Exercise, Quality of Life, and Mobility in Parkinson's Disease: A Longitudinal Analysis of National Parkinson Foundation Quality Improvement Initiative Data," *Journal of Parkinson's Disease*, 7(1) (2017): 193–202.

162. Michael J. Hove and Peter E. Keller, "Impaired Movement Timing in Neurological Disorders: Rehabilitation and Treatment Strategies," *Annals of the New York Academy of Sciences* 1337(1) (March 2015): 111–17.

163. Michael Rossato-Bennett, *Alive Inside* (documentary film, Projector Media, 2014).

164. Paulson et al., "Music and the Mind: The Magical Power of Sound."

165. Richard Robinson, "Parkinson's Disease: The Latest Developments in Targeting Alpha-Synuclein Spread, Inhibiting Glucocerebrosidease Mutations, and Fetal Transplant Autopsies," *Neurology Today* 16(24) (December 22, 2016): 27–29.

166. Shuchi Mittal et al., "β2-Adrenoreceptor Is a Regulator of the A-Synuclein Gene Driving Risk of Parkinson's Disease," *Science* 357(6354) (September 1, 2017): 891–98.

167. Elazer R. Edelman and Brittany N. Weber, "Tenuous Tether," *New England Journal of Medicine* 373 (December 3, 2015); 2199–2201.

168. Ibid.

169. Susan L. Mitchell, "Advanced Dementia," *New England Journal of Medicine* 372 (June 25, 2015): 2533–40.

170. Claudia L. Satizabal et al., "Incidence of Dementia over Three Decades in the Framingham Heart Study," *New England Journal of Medicine* (February 11, 2016): 523–32.

171. Mitchell, "Advanced Dementia".

172. Oliver Sacks, *Musicophilia: Tales of Music and the Brain:* 372-373.

173. Rossato-Bennett, *Alive Inside.*

174. Christina Geroldi et al., "Pop Music and Frontotemporal Dementia," *Neurology* 55(12) (December 26, 2000): 1935-6.

175. Hans Fantel, "SOUND; Poignance Measured in Digits," *New York Times*, July 16, 1989.

176. Maynard Solomon, *Beethoven* (New York, Schirmer Books, 1977), pp. 113–14.

177. Emily Underwood, "The Polluted Brain," *Science* 355(6323) (January 27, 2017): 342–45.

178. Rachel T. Buxton et al, "Noise Pollution Is Pervasive in U.S. Protected Areas," *Science* 356(6337) (May 5, 2017): 531–33.

179. Roger Chou et al., Screening Adults Aged 50 Years or Older for Hearing Loss: A Review of the Evidence for the U.S. Preventive Services Task Force," *Annals of Internal Medicine* 154(5) (March 1, 2011): 347–55.

180. Yuri Agrawal, Elizabeth A. Platz, and John K. Niparko, "Prevalence of Hearing Loss and Differences by Demographic Characteristics among US Adults: Data from the National Health and Nutrition Examination Survey, 1999–2004," *Archives of of Internal Medicine* 168(14) (July 28, 2008): 1522–30.

181. David Owen, "Pardon? High-Tech Hope for the Hard of Hearing," *The New Yorker*, April 3, 2017, pp. 38–44.

182. Navzer D. Engineer et al., "Reversing Pathological Neural Activity

Using Targeted Plasticity," *Nature* 470(7332) (February 3, 2011): 101–4; Jay A. Blundon et al., "Restoring Auditory Cortex Plasticity in Adult Mice by Restricting Thalamic Adenosine Signaling," *Science* 356(6345) (June 30, 2017):1352–56; and Kendra L. Marks et al., "Auditory-Somatosensory Bimodal Stimulation Desynchronizes Brain Circuitry to Reduce Tinnitus in Guinea Pigs and Humans," *Science Translational Medicine* 10(422) (January 3, 2018), pii: eaal3175.

183. Remy Wenmaekers et al., "Why Orchestral Musicians Are Bound to Wear Earplugs: About the Ineffectiveness of Physical Measures to Reduce Sound Exposure," *Journal of the Acoustical Society of America* 142(5) (November 2017): 3154–64.

184. Jesper Hvass Schmidt et al., "Sound Exposure of Symphony Orchestra Musicians," *Annals of Occupational Hygiene* 55(8) (October 2011): 893–905.

185. Michael S. Donnenberg et al., "The Sound That Failed," *American Journal of Medicine* 108(6) (April 15, 2000): 475–80.

186. Richard Rothenberg, Gary Becker, and Richard Wiet, "Syphilitic Hearing Loss," *Southern Medical Journal* 72(2) (March 1979): 118–20.

187. Nina Kraus and Travis White-Schwoch, "Neurobiology of Everyday Communication: What Have We Learned from Music?" *The Neuroscientist*, 23(3) (June 2016), pp. 287–98.

188. Frank R. Lin et al., "Hearing Loss and Cognitive Decline among Older Adults," *JAMA Internal Medicine* 173(4) (February 25, 2013): 293–99.

189. Stuart Isacoff, *Temperament: How Music Became a Battleground for the Great Minds of Western Civilization* (New York: Vintage, 2003); and Ross W. Duffin, *How Equal Temperament Ruined Harmony (And Why You Should Care)* (New York, Norton, 2007).

190. James Lecky, "Temperament," in *A Dictionary of Music and Musicians*, ed. George Grove (London: Macmillan, 1890), vol. 4, p. 73. "By constantly listening to the equally tempered scale, the ear may be brought, not only to tolerate its intervals, but to prefer them to those of any other system, at least as far as melody is concerned."

191. Isacoff, *Temperament*.

192. Bruce Haynes, *A History of Performing Pitch: The Story of "A"* (Lanham, MD: Scarecrow Press, 2002), Introduction, 0-1b.

193. James Lecky, "Temperament," in *A Dictionary of Music and Musicians*, ed. George Grove (London: Macmillan, 1890), vol. 4, p. 73. "By constantly listening to the equally tempered scale, the ear may be brought, not only to tolerate its intervals, but to prefer them to those of

any other system, at least as far as melody is concerned."

194. Ross Duffin, p. 155.

195. Peter F. Ostwald, with Lise Deschamps Ostwald, *Schumann: The Inner Voices of a Musical Genius*, p. 89.

196. Hans-Christian Jabusch and Eckart Altenmüller, "Epidemiology, Phenomenology and Therapy of Musician's Cramp," *Music, Motor Control and the Brain* (July 2006): 265–82.

197. Eckart O. Altenmüller, "From Laetoli to Carnegie: Music Making as a Paradigm for the Wonders of Neuroplasticity" (thesis): 21

198. Bernhard Haslinger et al., "Sensorimotor Overactivity as a Pathophysiologic Trait of Embouchure Dystonia," *Neurology* 74(22) (June 1, 2010): 1790–7.

199. Steven J. Frucht, "Embouchure Dystonia: A Video Guide to Diagnosis and Evaluation," *Journal of Clinical Movement Disorders* 3:10 (June 18, 2016).

200. Hans-Christian Jabusch and Eckart Altenmüller, "Focal Dystonia in Musicians: From Phenomenology to Therapy," *Advances in Cognitive Psychology* 2, 2–3 (2006): 207–20.

201. Haslinger et al., "Sensorimotor Overactivity as a Pathophysiologic Trait of Embouchure Dystonia".

202. Steven J. Frucht, Evaluating the musician with dystonia of the upper limb: a practical approach with video demonstration. *Journal of Clinical Movement Disorders* 2:16 (2015).

203. David Vining, *Chamber Music Magazine* (Fall 2012), p. 81.

204. Jay A. Blundon et al., 1352-1366.

205. Shiro Horisawa, et al., Safety and long-term efficacy of ventro-oral thalamotomy for focal hand dystonia: A retrospective study of 171 patients. *Neurology 92* (2019), 371-377.

206. Raymond W. Apple Jr., "Elected Bodies with Hardly a Cultured Bone," *New York Times*, July 26, 1998.

207. Peter Dobrin, "The Philadelphia Orchestra Needs to Rethink Its Future," *The Inquirer*, October 18, 2015.

208. Richard Brody, "Now Playing," *The New Yorker*, Aug 7 & 14, 2017, p. 12.

209. William Weber, *The Great Transformation of Musical Taste*: 199.

210. Richard Taruskin, Richard Taruskin, "The Modern Sound of Early Music": 169.

211. Alec Wilkinson, "Time is a Ghost: Vijay Iyer's Jazz Vision."

212. https://www.scribd.com/document/265348695/Microsoft-Attention-Spans-Research-Report.

213. Erin C. Tarver, "College Football Is Here. But What Are We Really Cheering?" *New York Times*, The Stone, August 21, 2017.

214. Charles Rosen, "The Future of Music," *New York Review of Books*, December 20, 2001.

215. Philip Clark, "What's Wrong with the Classical Concert Experience in the 21st Century," *Gramophone*, October 19, 2015.

216. David Brooks, "This Century Is Broken," *New York Times*, February 21, 2017.

217. Jed Gaylin, "Being Relevant—Who Cares?" October 5, 2015 at https://jedgaylin.com/being-relevant-who-cares/.

218. Ibid.

219. Adam Gopnik, "Music to Your Ears," *The New Yorker*, January 28, 2013, p. 32.

220. Eric William Lin, "Pulsecheck: Is Orchestral Music Still a Living Art Form in 2017? Extrapolating trends from 175 Seasons at the New York Philharmonic" (November 2017).

221. Andrew Decker, Stephanie Carter, "Ballet Austin: Expanding Audiences for Unfamiliar Works" (Wallace Foundation, February, 2017), http://www.wallacefoundation.org/knowledge-center/pages/ballet-austin-building-audiences-for-sustainability.aspx.

222. Matthew J. Salganik, Peter S. Dodds, and Duncan J. Watts, "Experimental Study of Inequality and Unpredictability in an Artificial Cultural Market," *Science* 311 (February 10, 2006): 854–56.

223. Farhad Manjoo, "I Ignored Trump News for a Week. Here's What I Learned," *New York Times*, February 22, 2017.

224. Kevin N. Laland, *Darwin's Unfinished Symphony How Culture Made the Human Mind*, p. 39.

225. Rosen, "The Future of Music".

226. Kelly Crow, "A Doctor in the Museum," *Wall Street Journal*, October 23, 2015.

227. Rosen, "The Future of Music".

228. Malinda Carpenter, "Instrumental, Social and Shared Goals and Intentions in Imitation," in *Imitation and the Social Mind: Autism and Typical Development*, ed. Sally J. Rogers & Justin H. G. Williams (New York: Guilford Press, 2006), pp. 48–70.

229. Anthony Mazzocchi, "Why Students Really Quit Their Musical Instrument (and How Parents Can Prevent It)," The Music Parents' Guide, February 17, 2015, http://www.musicparentsguide.com/2015/02/17/students-really-quit-musical-instrument-parents-can-prevent/.

230. Richard Taruskin, "The Modern Sound of Early Music," in *Text*

and Act, p. 170.

231. Dobrin, "The Philadelpia Orchestra Needs to Rethink Its Future".

232. Jonathan Mahler, "Is the Game Over?" *New York Times*, September 28, 2013.

233. Neil McLachlan et al., "Consonance and Pitch," *Journal of Experimental Psychology. General* 142(4) (November 2013): 1142–58; and Clive Paget, "Is Musical Beauty in the Brain of the Beholder?" *Limelight*, February 18, 2013.

234. At: John Adams, "John Adams Dishes on Pop Culture," FORA.tv, https://www.youtube.com/watch?v=h65aDay1znc.

235. Pew Research Center, "Sharp Partisan Divisions in Views of National Institutions: Republicans Increasingly Say Colleges Have Negative Impact on U.S.," Pew Research Center, July 10, 2017, http://www.people-press.org/2017/07/10/sharp-partisan-divisions-in-views-of-national-institutions/.

236. Eve L. Ewing, "Why Authoritarians Attack the Arts," *New York Times*, April 6, 2017.

237. Wendy Steiner, *The Scandal of Pleasure: Art in an Age of Fundamentalism* (Chicago: University of Chicago Press, 1995).

238. Richard Taruskin, *The Danger of Music and Other Anti-Utopian Essays* (Berkeley: University of California Press, 2008).

239. James Kennaway, *Bad Vibrations. The History of the Idea of Music as a Cause of Disease.*

240. Craig A. Monson, *Divas in the Convent: Nuns, Music, and Defiance in Seventeenth-Century Italy* (Chicago: University of Chicago Press, 2012).

241. Craig A. Monson, *Nuns Behaving Badly: Tales of Music, Magic, Art, & Arson in the Convents of Italy* (Chicago: University of Chicago Press, 2010).

242. Ewing, "Why Authoritarians Attack the Arts".

243. Ross Douthat, "Who Are We?" *New York Times*, February 4, 2017.

244. Ibid.

245. Ewing, "Why Authoritarians Attack the Arts".

246. John Eliot Gardiner, "The Class of '85," in *Bach: Music in the Castle of Heaven* (New York, Knopf, 2013): epigraph, chapter 8.

247. Perhaps a predecessor on a neighboring island led the way. The muse Terpsichore ("delight in the chorus"; 1st half 7th century BCE), probably the first human musician in Greek and Western music history, invented, or at least systematized, ancient Greek music, created choral poetry, and perfected the lyre by converting it from a four- to a sev-

en-stringed instrument (a development, according to Lawrence Durrell, "as decisive as the jump from clavichord to piano").

248. Alain de Botton, "How Fiction Ruined Love," *Financial Times*, April 22, 2016.

249. Franco Pisano and Gianni Boncompagni, "Tuca Tuca," recorded by Pink Martini in *Splendor in the Grass*, 2008.

250. Andrew Flanagan, "What Does Music Do to Us When We Listen to Music Together? Neuroscientist Daniel Levitin Helps Sonos Find Out: Q&A, February 9, 2016, at: http://www.billboard.com/articles/news/6867464/neuroscientist-daniel-levitin-sonos-listening-study-qa.

251. Steve Paulson et al., "Music and the Mind: The Magical Power of Sound," *Annals of the New York Academy of Sciences* 1303 (November 2013): pp. 63–79.

252. Szymon Laks, *Music of another World* (Evanston: Northwestern University Press, 1989).

253. Carrie Battan, "The Appeal of the Coachella Way of Life," *The New Yorker*, April 18, 2016.

254. David Remnick, "We are Alive", *The New Yorker*, July 30, 2012. https://www.newyorker.com/magazine/2012/07/30/we-are-alive.

255. Allison Babka, "Sex and the Symphony: Ben Folds Explains Why Orchestral Music Is the Best Aphrodisiac," *Riverfront Times*, April 9, 2014.

256. Ibid.

257. Janet Malcolm, "Yuja Wang and the Art of Performance," *The New Yorker*, September 5, 2016.

258. Nancy B. Reich, *Clara Schumann: The Artist and the Woman* (Ithaca & London: Cornell University Press, 1985). p. 214.

259. Liszt Ferenc Memorial Museum and Research Center: http//www.lisztmuseum.hu/en/exhibitions/.

260. Charles Rosen, *The Romantic Generation*. (Cambridge: Harvard University Press, 1995), pp. 491-492.

261. Chia-Jung Tsay, "Sight Over Sound in the Judgment of Music Performance," *Proceedings of the National Academy of Sciences of the United States of America* 110(36) (September 3, 2013): 14580–5.

262. Maria Corley, personal communication, 2017.

263. Hadju, "Forever Young? In Some Ways, Yes".

264. http://chq.org/about-us/our-mission.

265. Chorong Song, Harumi Ikei, and Yoshifumi Miyazaki, "Physiological Effects of Nature Therapy: A Review of the Research in Japan," *International Journal of Environmental Research and Public Health* 13(8)

(August 2016).

266. Edward O. Wilson, *The Biophilia Hypothesis* (Washington, DC: Island Press, 1993).

267. Song, Ikei, and Miyazaki, "Physiological Effects of Nature Therapy: A Review of the Research in Japan".

268. Jeffrey M. Craig, Alan C. Logan, and Susan L. Prescott, Natural Environments, Nature Relatedness and the Ecological Theater: Connecting Satellites and Sequencing to Shinrin-yoku," *Journal of Physiological Anthropology* 35(1) (January 2016): 1.

269. Peter Wohlleben, *The Hidden Life of Trees,* p. 221.

270. Katherine J. Willis and Gillian Petrokofsky, "The Natural Capital of City Trees," <u>Science</u> 356(6336) (April 28, 2017): pp. 374–76; and Florence Williams, The Nature Fix: Why Nature Makes Us Happier, Healthier, and More Creative, New York, W.W. Norton & Company, 2017.

271. Thomas Bulfinch, *Bulfinch's Mythology* (New York: Random House, 1998), pp. 32–33.

272. Higham et al., "Testing Models for the Beginnings of the Aurignacian and the Advent of Figurative Art and Music".

273. Richard Taruskin, *The Oxford History of Western Music*, vol. 3, "Music in the Nineteenth Century" (New York, Oxford University Press, 2010), p. 230-234.

274. Ibid.

275. Thomas Forrest Kelly, *First Nights: Five Musical Premieres,* (New Haven, Yale University Press, 2000), p. 256.

276. Isaiah Berlin, Shostakovich at Oxford, T*he New York Review of Books,* July 16, 2009.

277. Richard Taruskin, *The Oxford History of Western Music*, vol. 5, "Music in the Late Twentieth Century" (New York, Oxford University Press, 2010), p. 464.

278. Tanya Kevorkian, "The Reception of the Cantata during Leipzig Church Services, 1700–1750," *Early Music*, February 202, pp. 26–44.

279. Arnold Steinhardt, quoted in *The Art of Quartet Playing: The Guarneri Quartet in Conversation with David Blum* (New York: Knopf, 1986), p. 28.

280. Jon Meacham, *Thomas Jefferson: The Art of Power* (New York: Random House, 2012).

281. Helen Cripe, *Thomas Jefferson and Music* (Charlottesville, VA: University Press of Virginia, 1973), Page 32 is about practice.

282. *Jefferson Himself: The Personal Narrative of a Many-Sided American*, ed. Bernard Mayo (Charlottesville, VA: University Press of Virgin-

ia, 1942).
283. Ibid., p. 42.
284. Ibid., p. 31.
285. Helen Cripe, *Thomas Jefferson and Music* p. 90.
286. Ibid., p. 8.
287. Alex Ross, *The Rest Is Noise: Listening to the Twentieth Century* (New York: Farrar, Straus and Giroux; 2007), p. 343.
288. Richard Conniff, "The Fraud Detective," *Yale Alumni Magazine,* September/October 2013.
289. Joe Nocera, "The Man Who Got China Right," *The New York Times*, August 23, 2015.
290. Thomas, *On Matters of Doubt.*
291. Gopnik, "Music to Your Ears," p. 32.
292. Andrew Flanagan, "What Does Music Do to Us When We Listen to Music Together? Neuroscientist Daniel Levitin Helps Sonos Find Out: Q&A.
293. Gopnik, "Music to Your Ears," p. 32.

Acknowledgements

I never adequately thanked the most important mentors in my life. I apologize belatedly for having taken many of their efforts for granted.

Harlan Thomas taught me in the fifth grade how to play a scale on the flute and led the ensembles I played it in all the way through high school. John Stavash taught me the fundamentals of music making and wind playing. He arrived at my house every week after school, usually late, but then stayed far longer than the allotted hour. Joseph Maddy over four summers at Interlochen convinced me that I could become a professional musician. Joseph Mariano helped me master the flute repertoire at Eastman every Saturday afternoon for four years, even though I had appeared at his studio during my first week in college oblivious to the fact all his other new students had submitted audition tapes during the previous year. My roommate and bassoonist Robert Horick and close friend and eager accompanist Jerry Bramblett taught me about music and many other things in life.

Yale Medical School convinced me that medical school is not for stuffing the brain with information but instead a way to kindle a lifelong process of listening to humans in distress, understanding their lives and diseases, and a quest to eventually attain the judgement, knowledge, and wisdom to provide effective care. TR Johns, MD, introduced me to the wonders of the nervous system and showed me how to be a neurologist. Martin Netsky, MD, taught me how to write well in English, plan a research project, and look at the brain through a microscope. Jack Greenberg, MD, taught me how to examine the brain with MRI and run an imaging practice. Don Jaeger made sure there was always an orchestra or music festival for me to play in. The staff at Lebanon Magnetic Imaging and the hundreds of board members and staff at Gretna Music provided much of my postgraduate education in medicine and music. Suzanne Stewart, Carl Kane, Nadeen Van Tuyle, Allen Krantz, Susan Hostetter offered good insight into the writing and content of this book and many other things.

My editor, Robert Cohen, greatly improved the original draft, helped me make my prose clear, interesting, and readable, and gave me respect for the Oxford comma. Marj Charlier, whom Emi and I met at her living-room piano across our lawn in an amazing bolt of serendipity, helped me illustrate, edit, publish, and sell this book.

My lovely wife, Emi, a soprano, gave me not only useful suggestions, but also countless hours of solitude in order to finish the project.

Index

Laks, Szymon, 26, 165
Laland, Kevin, 16
Lecky, James, 113, 115
Lederer, Doris, 230
Leonardo, 104
Leventhal, David, 83
Levin, Meyer, 248, 250
Levitin, Daniel, 43, 165, 176
Lexington, Michigan, 224
Lion King, The, 229
Lipman, Samuel, 253
Liszt, Franz, 6, 50, 155, 169-171
Lobanova-Heasley, Inna, 213
Los Angeles Philharmonic, 59, 139, 183
Lowell, James Russell, 253
Lucerne Festival, 18, 95-96, 172

Maddy, Joseph E., 182, 287
Mahler, Gustav, 18, 43, 95-96, 125, 150, 164, 172, 175, 222
Malcolm, Janet, 168, 284
Mark Morris Dance Company, 83
Marlboro, 143, 191
Mars, Bruno, 144, 167
McPartland, Marian, 44, 175, 261
melisma, 214
Mendelssohn, Felix, 14
Mercury, 205-206
Merriam, A. P., 43
Metallica, 106
Metropolitan Opera, 45, 164, 176, 223, 232
Micromusics of the West, 29
Mills, Irving, 8
MIT (Massachusetts Institute of Technology), 36, 45
MIT (Melodic Intonation Therapy), 70-71
Mithen, Steven, 12
Mizler, Lorenz Christoph, 158
Monson, Craig, 154
Monticello, 242

Mormons, 14
Moscow Conservatory, 215-216
Moscow State University, 209
Mosquito, sound repeller, 100
Mournay, Gabriel, 206-207
Moyse, Marcel, 88
Mozart, Wolfgang Amadeus, 39, 42, 114, 144, 157, 221-222, 242, 260
MRI (definitions), 33
Mussorgsky, Modeste, 181, 212

neuroplasticity, 35, 54, 115, 265
Neurostaff, 83-84
New Black Eagle Jazz Band, 201
Newton, Isaac, 38
Nogo receptor, 55

O'Keefe, Georgia, 20
Ojai Festival, 143
Oklahoma City Symphony, 44
Ornstein, Doris, 254-257
ossicles, 101, 104
Oundjian, Peter, 124
Oxford History of Western Music, 137, 209

Pachelbel, Johann, 142
Page, Patti, 177
Paisiello, Giovanni, 212
Parkinson's Disease, 3, 69, 76, 79-85, 93, 128
Patel, Aniruddh, 5, 22-23
Paul, Les, 177
Pennsylvania Council on the Arts, 191
Pennsylvania Dutch, 157, 196
Peretz, Isabelle, 22
Peter Ostwald, 120
Peter the Great, 213
philéo, 161
Philadelphia Orchestra, 199, 202
Philosophy, Hall of, 200, 202
Pink Martini, 163

ABOUT THE AUTHOR

Dr. Ellenberger studied flute performance at the Eastman School of Music as a premed student at the University of Rochester. He performed in the New Haven Symphony, the Yale Collegium Musicum, and the Yale Symphonic Wind Ensemble while getting his medical degree at the Yale School of Medicine. As a faculty member at Penn State's College of Medicine he was principal flutist in the Harrisburg Symphony. Today, he works with Gretna Music, which he founded forty-four years ago and has been named "one of six of the best small music festivals in the U.S." by Time Magazine.

CPSIA information can be obtained
at www.ICGtesting.com
Printed in the USA
LVHW091504310120
645461LV00004B/80/J